Potters

Seventh Edition

Potters

Edited by Emmanuel Cooper and Eileen Lewenstein

An illustrated directory of the work of full members of the Craftsmen Potters Association of Great Britain

A guide to pottery training in the United Kingdom

Seventh Edition

The Craftsmen Potters Association of Great Britain

Individual entries in the directory have been supplied
by the members concerned.

Edited by Emmanuel Cooper and Eileen Lewenstein
assisted by Daphne Matthews and Marilyn Brown.

Pottery training section is a revised version of that which appeared in
Studio Ceramics Today.

Cover — detail of platter by Janice Tchalenko

Photographs supplied by potters or from Ceramic Review

Book design by Ceramic Review

Potters

First Edition	1972
Second Edition	1974
Third Edition	1975
Fourth Edition	1977
Fifth Edition	1980
Sixth Edition	1983
Seventh Edition	1986

ISBN 0 9504767 4 9

Published by the Craftsmen Potters Association of Great Britain Ltd.
William Blake House, Marshall Street, London WIV IFD
©Craftsmen Potters Association 1986
Printed by Bushey Mead Press Ltd., Hailsham, England.

Contents

Introduction

'Potters' the illustrated directory of the work of full members of the Craftsmen Potters Association continues to be a useful guide to pottery in the United Kingdom. This, the seventh edition has been completely revised and given a new format. For the first time illustrations of potters at work in their studios are included, as well as their work. This change reflects the greater interest in the maker as well as the object, and is a clear indication of the changing status of the craft.

Names, addresses and telephone numbers of all full members of the Craftsmen Potters Association of Great Britain are listed on pages 156-169 together with details of visiting times, showroom opening and so on – invaluable information for anyone planning a visit. Some potters welcome callers to their showrooms and workshops and some allow visitors to their showrooms only. This information is clearly stated together with the opening hours. Many of the potters have indicated that they welcome visitors, but by appointment only. If you wish to visit a potter who can only see you by appointment please write or telephone beforehand. A specially drawn map shows where workshops and studios open to the public are situated. Between pages 10-154 are illustrations of potters and their pots, together with a brief description of the type of work they make. Biographical notes are supplied by the potters themselves, and photographs illustrate recent work. Workshop and individual potters marks are included as an aid to identification.

The section 'So you want to be a Potter' on pottery training lists degree and vocational courses available at art schools, colleges and institutes of higher education. It also contains information on part-time study. There is also useful advice on how to apply to work with potters in their workshops.

The Craftsmen Potters Association is the largest organization of studio potters in Britain and has 149 full members all of whom are professional potters. We are sure that this new edition will prove to be as useful a guide to pottery in the United Kingdom as the previous ones. Every effort has been made to ensure that the information included is correct at the time of printing.

The Craftsmen Potters Association

The Craftsmen Potters Association was formed in 1958 as a co-operative to sell the work of its potter members and to increase general awareness of the craft. In 1955 purchase tax extended to include domestic ware. This led Walter Lipton who was then at the Rural Industries Bureau, in a move to help potters, to arrange an exhibition of pottery for export; it was bought complete by a New Zealand store. This success prompted a group of potters to appoint a working party to consider ways and means of forming an association that could organize similar activities.

Under the guidance of Walter Lipton the Craftsmen Potters Association was formed as an Industrial and Provident Society – Rosemary Wren was elected the first chairman and David Canter was appointed Honorary Secretary. The organisation is democratic; upon election each full member buys a £1 share and is entitled to elect Council Members and to vote at the Annual General Meeting. Policy decisions are made at Council Meetings when ideas from full and associate members are discussed.

Shop History

The Council decided to open a shop selling the work of its members in the heart of London's West End. In the Spring of 1959 a lease was taken on premises at Lowndes Court, Carnaby Street, before the street gained its present fame. The interior of the shop and basement was built by a team of volunteers who worked in their free time for the following twelve months.

On May 30th 1960 the shop opened with a superb exhibition of Ray Finch's stoneware. The shop made steady progress; sales increased and its reputation became established. When the shop first opened a non-selective principle of membership was in operation. In an attempt to establish standards of craftsmanship, a system was introduced whereby applicants for full membership had to satisfy the Council's Selection Committee, which consists of all Council Members plus the Shop Manager, as to the quality of the work they send in. Council Members keep an eye on all work on show in the shop, and members can be asked to remove work considered unsuitable.

New Premises

In March 1966 the Association negotiated for and acquired larger shop premises in a building being erected in Marshall Street on the site of the house where William Blake was born. David Attenborough performed the opening ceremony of the new shop on December 4th 1967. The layout of the original shop was designed by David Canter: visitors to the shop could easily get to members stock-shelves as well as the general display area, to make their own selection. On the front of the counter was a ceramic relief panel by Eileen Nisbet. The fascia on the shop-front was designed by Donald Jackson in co-operation with Barry Guppy who modelled the letters in stoneware clay. It incorporated the CPA symbol designed by David Canter. In 1983 the interior of the shop was redesigned by Ron Carter, with the help of a grant from the Crafts Council. The established features were retained but the false ceiling was removed to give a more airy space and the members stock-shelves and new display tables were built in black elm in keeping with the changing needs of the shop. Outside, the hanging sign still contains the original saltglazed pot made by Rosemary Wren for the first shop.

The Craftsmen Potters Shop is managed by Vivien Whitaker with the help of full and part-time assistants. A large and varied selection of members work is always on show and special exhibitions are arranged. The Craftsmen Potters Shop is unique in Central London selling and exhibiting only studio pots. The shop also has a well-equipped sundries section which stocks sponges, cones, turning tools, cane handles, Japanese brushes, sieves etc. all at very competitive prices. A good range of books on pottery, all approved by the Council are on sale as well as postcards of specially photographed pots. Full, Associate and Junior Members are entitled to a 10% discount on all purchases except books.

Association Activities

As well as 149 full members, the Craftsmen Potters Association has an average of 500 associate members who contribute much to its activities. Many of the association's activities are the responsibility of sub-committees. The Archives sub-committee was headed by Robert Fournier until 1985 and was responsible for preserving photographic and visual records of pots, potters and potteries as well as recording exhibitions and collecting such things as price lists and information handouts. Evening meetings arranged by Vanessa Wills, association secretary, have included talks by eminent potters from both this country and overseas. Recent talks have been given by Harry Davis, James Tower and Oliver Watson. Special exhibitions at the Craftsmen Potters Shop have included mixed shows of members' work and solus exhibitions by individual members. Weekend events are arranged from time to time, the most recent of which was the two-day workshop by John Glick in London in September 1985. The association also arranges each week a 'Potter in the Shop', when members of the CPA talk or demonstrate in the shop for a day. This has proved to be highly popular enabling potter and public to meet informally to exchange information and advice. Associate members receive advance information of all these events, priority booking, reduced fees and invitations to private views of exhibitions.

Ceramic Review

The association publish the internationally acclaimed magazine 'Ceramic Review' a contemporary survey of studio pottery. It appears six times a year and has a wide circulation both in this country and abroad. Members can subscribe to the magazine at a reduced rate.

Ceramic Review Publications

An edition of 'The Ceramic Review Book of Clay Bodies and Glaze Recipes' has now been published. Enlarged and completely revised it includes over 400 recipes from professional potters and has much useful advice on mixing and using bodies and glazes.

Lead Release

The Craftsmen Potters Association is fully aware of the possible danger to health of cadmium or lead released from glazed pottery into food. Recent publicity has linked craft pottery with lead release. Because of this the CPA council now requires all members sending work to the shop to state whether lead or cadmium are used in their pottery or not. If these materials are present then potters must have their work tested regularly and produce certificates to show that it conforms to the British Standard BS4860. The public can buy safely from the CPA shop.

A full and detailed history of the Craftsmen Potters Association was included in Studio Ceramics Today published by the CPA in 1983 on the occasion of its Silver Jubilee.

Illustrated Directory of CPA members

Most full members of the Association have work on sale at the Craftsmen Potters Shop. A full list of members, together with names and addresses, can be found on page 156.

Adrian Abberley

Adrian Abberley works alone making individual pieces and some domestic ware in oxidised stoneware and porcelain, using combination of slab built and thrown sections.

John Ablitt. Born in Ipswich in 1945. Studied at Bristol 1964–68. I have a small workshop in Somerset which I share with my wife who knits and weaves silk. My working life is divided into three categories – designing for industry, teaching and making burnished pots. I like this diversity; I find it enriching, although it sometimes feels as if there are too many tops to keep spinning. At some point in the future I think that I will get involved in some sort of repetition work – possible domestic pottery or tile making. My burnished pots are made from Fremington clay, pressmoulded or thrown. When leather hard the pots are decorated with strongly stained ball clay slips. I use both oxides and commercial stains. Burnishing is done with a silver spoon, again at the leather hard stage. The work is fired in an electric kiln to Orton cone 05. Many things influence my work and these of course change over the years. I admire the quality of old wooden utensils, and ethnographic museums have always held a strong attraction. Textiles are also important, especially Middle Eastern kelims which I collect in a limited way.

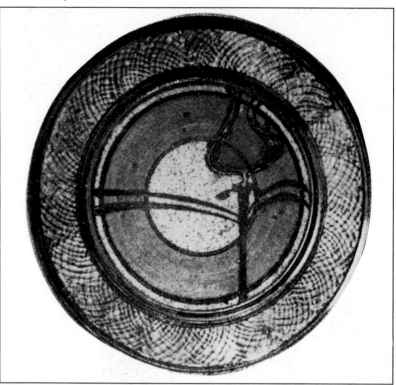

Mick Arnup. Born in the East End of London and educated at Coopers Company School in Bow. After war service with the RAF became a painting student at Kingston and the Royal College of Art. Teaching followed with responsibility for a small ceramics studio in York. Pottery had always been an important second study but a new interest was fostered when Henry Hammond made it possible for him to join the special group of potters on the Michael Cardew 'Pioneer Pottery' gathering at Wenford Bridge. Resigned teaching post in 1972 and built new workshops and showroom at Holtby. The 70 cu.ft. oil fired downdraught kiln was designed by David Lloyd Jones who gave advice and encouragement. The kiln was recently lined with 2" ceramic fibre which reduced fuel costs by 30%. Ceramic signs and numerals, large garden pots and domestic pieces are produced with occasional help from assistants. But the decorated plates (some of which are as large as 24 inches) exploiting the textural richness and sonorous colour of high temperature glazes in a painterly way, form the most important part of his output. Sales are made through selected galleries and the Holtby showroom which is shared with his wife, the sculptor Sally Arnup, with whom he exhibits both in the United Kingdom and abroad. Painting is still a commitment in the search for a personal method of pot decoration.

Chris Aston

Chris Aston has been a full-time working potter for twenty years, with a studio and showroom in converted farm buildings adjacent to his 18th Century cottage at Elkesley, on the edge of Sherwood Forest and Robin Hood country, in North Nottinghamshire. Of the 18,000 pots produced here each year, Chris strikes a balance between domestic and exhibition work, with a workshop routine of volume throwing interspersed with periods of more time-consuming individual throwing and finishing, with a glaze firing approximately every two weeks. He enjoys the discipline of making repeat pots in quantity, believing that this is the only stable and fluent base from which to make his more individual work, which is exhibited widely. All his pots have a very characteristic form and decoration, with an increasing emphasis on the use of copper, both under other glazes and as the most dominant ingredient of the glaze itself. Used under his glazes, the copper volatilises to form dark-centred dots surrounded by rosy haloes, and this effect is used widely not only in his domestic ware, but also with brushwork, geometric designs, and landscape line drawings on large bowls, cut-sided dishes, and wall-hanging plates. Chris also enjoys the scientific and technical aspects of pottery-making, and works continually to maintain and improve the quality of his glazes and clay bodies, using chemical analysis and molecular formulae. The pottery itself is on the A1 twenty miles north of Newark.

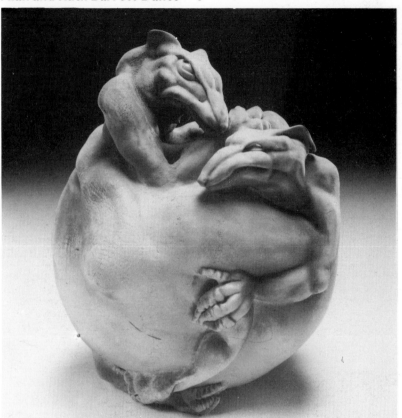

Alan and Ruth Barrett-Danes' work falls into two areas; (1) individual pots which include pedestal bowls and lidded pedestal pots. The glazes are mostly in-glaze lustre applied over vitrified biscuit slips. The decoration is achieved by spraying in-glaze lustre through stencils contrasting with the surface quality of the vitreous slip. (2) Individual modelled pieces, based on thrown forms which are softened and manipulated into the total structure. The stages in the development of each piece are complex involving hand modelling, carving and sometimes pressmoulded additions. The piece is fired to 1000°C and then the colour is developed on the form by a combination of spraying and painting using vitreous slips. The piece may be fired several times to achieve the desired colouration. The only glaze used is on the eye of the animal. In both areas there is a strong interest in the application and innovation of surface qualities related to functional and non-functional ceramic form.

Svend Bayer makes woodfired stoneware garden pots and kitchen pots.

Michael Bayley

MB

Michael Bayley makes a range of stoneware comprising various pot forms, press-moulded bowls and wall-pieces. Each form is essentially sculptural, being hand-built and having a rock-like presence due to the rugged, unglazed surface and rich earth-coloured markings. His work reflects his love of natural form. Landscape, mountains, rocks, trees, the seashore, skyscapes and the shapes, tones and markings associated with these, influence almost everything he makes. His starting point is clay made rough by the addition of grog and sand and tinted with iron or manganese, the colours ranging from light cream to warm, umbrous shades of brown. A number of different toned clays are laminated to produce striking 'agate' pattern. Tonal textures and pattern are made by rolling coloured clays into one another and afterwards 'inlaying'. Designs range from the abstract to effects with depth and form. On occasions pots are embellished with blue and white porcelain. All work is once fired to 1280°C. Apart from his evolving output of shapes, he enjoys working to commission. Bowls and platters, sculptural centre-pieces and wall-pieces (relief wall sculpture, tiles and panels) can be made to a client's particular requirements. Trained at Hornsey College of Art, London in the 1950s, his pots have been exhibited in various leading craft/ceramic galleries in both the U.K. and abroad and are represented in public and private collections in Europe and the U.S.A.

PFB

Peter Beard. Born in Southport, Lancashire, in 1951. Started working in potteries in 1965 which made items by casting and press moulding and which fired my interest in ceramics. Studied industrial design and furniture design at Ravensbourne College of Art, London 1970-73. Whilst at college continued interest in ceramics. In 1973 moved to Scotland to help set up a pottery making thrown domestic ware and started interest in one-off and sculptural pieces. Opened studio in Kent in 1975 making one-off pieces and sculpture. Became a member of the CPA in 1976 and moved to present studio in Kent in 1980. Present work is all thrown pieces with modelled additions but work is moving more towards predominantly hand building and on a larger scale. Bigger pots are nicer to make. Current work mostly has a manganese "gold" glaze although other colours are beginning to creep in. Some pots are of reduced porcelain with copper pink decoration but these are in the minority. Pots are predominantly porcelain but as things seem to be getting out of hand in scale, stoneware has come more to the fore. The clay is either T material or a mixture of ⅓ T material, ⅓ Craftcrank and ⅓ Ivanhoe, all by Potclays. Work is exhibited widely in England and abroad. Exhibitions include: One man shows at Volksbank, Einheim, West Germany 1979; Peter Dingley Gallery, Stratford, 1980; Rye City Art Gallery, Rye, 1981; Galerie An Gross St Martin, Köln, 1982; Liberty, London, 1984; Innate Harmony, London, 1985.

Terry Bell-Hughes. Born 1939 in Wales. Attended Abergele Junior School and Abergele Grammar School. Originally worked as a civil servant with Ministry of Agriculture in London. Studied painting part-time at Manresa College, Chelsea. Went to Teachers Training College, Barry, South Wales 1963. Taught in secondary schools. Joined the Harrow Pottery course 1967 under Victor Margrie and Michael Casson. First workshop with Trefor Owen in Shepherds Bush. Second workshop rented from Denise and Rosemary Wren, Potters Croft, Oxshott, Surrey until 1978. Moved back to Wales to set up present workshop with wife Beverley and four children. Primarily interested at present in domestic pots, thrown in series, and fired to 1280°C in reducing fire. All the pots are decorated with slips under ash or felspathic glazes. Decoration is derived from natural sources, necessarily adapted to forms. Exhibited in several one man and many shared exhibitions in Britain and abroad. Work included in several public and private collections.

Tony Benham

Tony Benham. During the summer of 1985, I made sketches on the coast near Folkestone and then developed slab forms from these ideas. The pebble and rock shapes have hollows and openings for plants. Some over 18 inches high are also indoor waterfalls. As my building technique develops the forms will become much larger. The clay body is prepared from powdered materials including local clay. The glazes are both slip and hop ash, fired in a gas kiln to 1270°C.

Maggie Angus Berkowitz   II

Maggie Angus Berkowitz paints pictures on tiles, using glazes and oxides, poured, trailed, carved, incised, inlaid, using multiple firings, wax and latex resists, and any other technique she might find or invent for a particular project. Tile panels may be of any size, the largest she has worked on so far being an 11' high panel for Great Ormond Street Hospital. Tiles used are Dennis Ruabon quarries, Woolliscroft ironstone − vitrified and weather-proof for floors and outside walls, or industrial wall blanks for interior surfaces. After living, studying, teaching and working in schools, factories and workshops around the world (Ambleside and London, Salerno and Faenza, Tanzania, New York) she returned to home ground on the edge of the Lake District twelve years ago. Has since taught, brought up children, exhibited regularly mostly in the North West − Abbot Hall, Lancaster City Museum, Haworth Art Gallery, Gawthorpe Hall and with the Guild of Lakeland Craftsmen, and at the Victoria and Albert Museum. Has worked full-time as ceramist since 1983, and commissions have included panels for Langdale Estate Timeshare, Burlington Slate Company Head Office, TAVR Centre Newton Aycliffe, and various domestic installations. She discusses projects with clients and will incorporate their ideas and suggestions, taking them, along with the architectural considerations, not as limitations on, but stimuli to design. Prices for individual pieces range from £200 for a small domestic panel. Estimates are given for larger projects and work can be planned within a budget.

Audrey Blackman

Audrey Blackman's human and animal sculptures are all rolled, mainly in porcelain bisque with marbled, inlaid and impressed decoration using stained clays in many colours. Her figures can be seen at the Fitzwilliam Museum, Cambridge; the City of Stoke-on-Trent Museum; the Cecil Higgins Museum in Bedford; the Crafts Study Centre at the Holburne Museum in Bath; the Oxford City and County Museum and at the Taipei Fine Arts Museum in Taiwan. Her abstract sculpture in stoneware and stained glass is in the Pilkington Glass Museum at St Helens, Lancs. She began her work in glazed earthenware, moved on to slip-decorated earthenware unglazed, then stoneware stained in several colours and unglazed and finally porcelain. Audrey Blackman describes the technique step by step in her book *Rolled Pottery Figures* (A and C Black), the German translation *Figuren aus Ton in Rolltechnik* (Hörnemann Verlag) and the Dutch version *Boetseren met kleirollen* (Gaade). The technique can be watched in every detail on three video tapes available from Peter Thomas, 16 Farm Road, Abingdon, Oxon., tel: (0235) 25184. The first shows the making of a figure from start to finish. The second is an exhibition of her work from the earliest to the latest and the third is specifically a teaching tape called "Basic Techniques". Her current prices range from £150–£250. Each work is signed "A Blackman", dated and numbered. She was Chairman of the Society of Designer-Craftsmen 1967-70 and is a member of the International Academy of Ceramics.

Clive Bowen. The pottery was established in 1971. The pots are thrown in red earthenware clay and range from large scale store jars and garden pots to mugs and egg cups. The domestic ware and one-off pots may be decorated with three contrasting slips, using slip trailing, combing and sgraffito methods. The pots are once-fired in a round (8' dia.) down-draught wood-fired kiln to 1040°C–1060°C (less for garden pots).

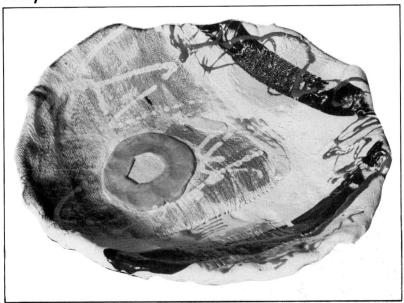

Sandy Brown. I cannot believe my luck. For years I had felt myself to be totally uncreative, but now, since the expressive tap was turned on in Japan 15 years ago, I am amazed at what comes out of me. The Crafts Council have been extremely good to me, first by giving me a generous grant in 1975, and then by sending me to the USA in 1985. I have been a visiting artist at the University of Texas, and have exhibited in Tokyo, Berlin, and New York. And I do like the fact that the *Sunday Times Magazine* has recommended me as being collectable. My work is stoneware, and is bold and dramatic and colourful. I use clay in a free way, and paint with natural oxides and commercial underglazes. My work is signed. I do all sorts of things. Today, for example, I have in progress: 1. A Bird God. 2. Two big abstract figurative dancers. 3. Clay 'paintings' of my dreams. 4. Abstract expressionist slabs of clay imprinted with cardboard, cloth, keys, etc; and added to with coils etc. They are draped over a round-bottomed cauldron, have feet added, and are painted and trailed over with coloured glazes. 5. A huge coiled pot, freely made, which is almost too big to go in the kiln. 6. Thrown bowls, soup tureens, teapots, and cups and saucers. 7. Octagon dinner plates, slab made over a wooden former. 8. Lasagne dishes; slab made, rectangular. 9. A self-portrait made blindfold, which looks like an Easter Island head with my mother's nose.

Ian Byers

Ian Byers was born 1947 in Birmingham. Trained at Central School of Art, London 1966-69. 1972-79 taught part-time and produced work varying from chess sets to ceramic jewellery and buttons for fashion house. 1979-1984 made raku pieces sold mainly through exhibitions. Work now contains some raku but also other firings and is more sculptured and three-dimensional than the patterned raku pieces. Some work has been stamped or incised with the symbol.

Alan Caiger-Smith works mostly in tin-glazed earthenware, thrown or press-moulded. Plates, and some standard bowls and mugs, are jolleyed. A few special forms are hand-built. Most of the work is painted (in-glaze) before being fired, or is decorated with reduced-pigment lustres, which need a third firing. All the lustreware and much of the other work is wood-fired. At irregular intervals some porcelain and semi-porcelain is also produced. The range of work extends from a steady but not rigidly repeated variety of domestic pottery and tiles to commissioned pieces and individual work, some of it large, which is possible because of the woodfired kiln. Alan started alone and later attracted a team of assistants, which now usually numbers seven or eight. His associate, Edgar Campden, has worked with him for 24 years and they have held a number of joint exhibitions. In 1985 the City Museum of Stoke-on-Trent put on a large retrospective exhibition covering the 30 years of Aldermaston Pottery, representing many facets of Alan's work, an extensive collection of Edgar's work, and groups of pots by other Aldermaston potters. The show will travel during 1986-7. The illustrated catalogue includes a detailed account of the Pottery and its members, the techniques, and the exhibitions at home and overseas from 1957 to 1985.

Daphne Carnegy

DC

Daphne Carnegy. I came to pottery by a fairly circuitous route, which included a French degree, publishing and teaching, and, like so many others, found myself almost by accident at a pottery evening class. Pottery became increasingly important to me and I was lucky enough to be offered a job with a *faience* potter in Burgundy. I worked there for a year and then worked in two other potteries in France, gaining valuable throwing and workshop experience. Feeling the need for a more formal art school training, I returned to England to take the Harrow Studio Pottery course. On leaving Harrow in 1980, I set up a workshop at Kingsgate Workshops, Kilburn and since then have been producing a range of functional, decorative tin-glazed earthenware. All pieces are thrown in a mixture of buff and red clays to give a warm apricot body. Oxides and underglaze colours are used to paint on to the freshly applied glaze and the glaze is then fired to 1140°C. I find the 'majolica' process continually challenging, not only because there are so many technical variables involved but also with regard to searching for a new vocabulary of painted decoration while retaining the feel of the European tradition. Influences are wide-flung and include early Islamic ware, European peasant pottery, textile patterns and plant forms. I sell to selected shops and galleries throughout the country and have participated in many group exhibitions. In February 1985, I had a solo exhibition at Fremantle Arts Centre, W. Australia.

Michael Casson 18

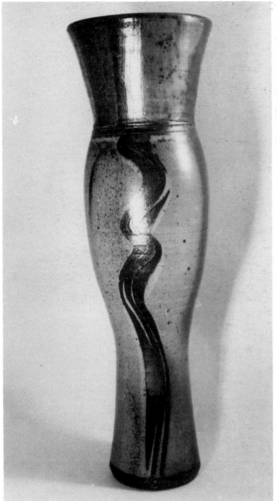

Michael Casson. First pots 1945, first workshop London 1952 (after NDD, ATD, Hornsey College of Art), earthenware, electric fired tin glazed figures and pots. Second workshop, Buckinghamshire 1959-77, domestic stoneware gas fired. Third, present, workshop 1977 — at first oil and now only wood-fired individual functional ware. Early member of CPA 1957/8, chairman mid 60s, council member until early 70s. Member of British Crafts Centre. Co-founder of Harrow studio-pottery course 1963 (with Victor Margrie). Founder board member of Dartington Pottery Training Workshop. President of Midland Potters Association; 1983 OBE; Currently committee member of Crafts Council. Books: *Pottery in Britain Today* 1966; *Craft of the Potter* 1976 (presenter of BBC TV series of same name 1975). Currently teaching, one day a week, history of ceramics at Cardiff College of Art; some workshops and lectures at home and abroad mainly America. Exhibitions held at intervals from 1959 onwards, home and abroad (Gold medal Prague 1964 Academy of Ceramic Arts). Work in main public and private collections. After many years of producing a full range of domestic stoneware with Sheila Casson now making more individual pieces of functional ware. Jugs, bowls and jars in several different shapes and sizes form the main work with some tall vase forms and more recently a new range of teapots. All the work is wood-fired, most is saltglazed; the teapots and some bowls are wood-fired porcelain.

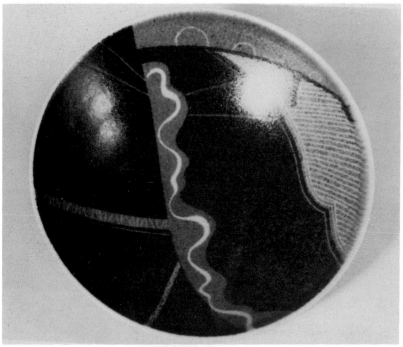

Sheila Casson. 1946-51 studied at Hornsey College of Art. NDD in Pottery and Lithography, ATD. 1955 shared workshop with Michael Casson in London making tinglazed earthenware. Early member of CPA 1958. 1959 Domestic stoneware oxidised in electric kiln, subsequently reduction fired in gas kiln. 1977 moved to present workshop in Herefordshire, making individual pieces in porcelain with decoration inspired by the Herefordshire landscape. The technique is a combination of sprayed slips with paper and latex resist and sgraffito. Bisc fired and then glazed in a reduction gas kiln to 1280°. Taken part in numerous exhibitions at the CPA and Casson Galley in London. Also Bluecoat Gallery, Liverpool, Collection Gallery, Ledbury, Newport Museum, Westminster Gallery Boston USA and the English Gallery and Heller Gallery West Germany.

Jenny Clarke trained at Farnham School of Art in the 1960s under Paul Barron and Henry Hammond. Shared a workshop in London with Sally Dawson for several years; during this time spent one summer working for David Leach. After a year in New Zealand in 1971, travelling and contacting different craftspeople – returned to England and started sharing a studio with Ian Godfrey. Moved to Bristol in 1974 where home and workshop are now combined. Produces a wide range of domestic stoneware, using iron slips and sgraffito decoration. At present concentrating more on individual porcelain pieces, using coloured inlays and spraying techniques for decoration. Exhibitions include Barclaycraft, Wandle and Long Street Galleries. Sells work in a number of craft galleries. Member of the Gloucestershire Guild of Craftsmen.

Derek Clarkson studied at Manchester and Burnley Schools of Art. Thirty years of lecturing in ceramics at Northern colleges and potting for exhibitions, now followed by full-time potting since 1980. Demonstration/lectures given by invitation. Working alone (sorry, does not take students) making individual pieces of decorative stoneware and porcelain; mainly bottles and bowls. Thrown, with turning a vital part of the making process. Firing is in a 12 cu.ft. gas kiln to 1300°C with a reducing atmosphere. A number of different bodies are used because a particular glaze/body combination gives a sought after quality, though in the main fine light firing ones. Smooth waxy cream wood ash glazes with cobalt and iron brush decoration predominate. Also wax resist using ash, celadon, kaki and tenmoku glazes. Titanium aventurine and copper red glazes are used with little or no decoration. Translucent porcelain bowls are incised, others brush decorated and on occasions given a third firing with burnished gold and enamels. Exhibitions national and international, from representing Great Britain at the International Academy of Ceramics, Geneva in 1965, to Studio Ceramics Today, Victoria and Albert Museum London in 1983. Work has also been included on the Design Council Index. Represented in many public galleries including the Victoria and Albert Museum and private collections.

Margery Clinton. Diploma in Drawing and Painting, Glasgow School of Art, MA Royal College of Art School of Ceramics, Member of Society of Designer Craftsmen. Pottery and tiles on Design Index, Design Centre London. I work with two assistants Christine and Evelyn, and together we produce a collection of containers, lamps and tiles mainly in the reduction lustre technique, which I have continued to develop since first beginning research at the Royal College in 1973. Range of work varies from special commissions like the figure of St. Andrew to an individually decorated lustre trinket box. My interest in light and decoration is I think fairly dominant in my work, but I do like to make things that also have a practical use. The latest in the container collection is a jardiniere in an allover lustre glaze. This is made in two sizes: 8" high and 5" high. The latest lamp is a wall light in porcelain. Most of the pottery is earthenware bisque fired to 1100°C and glazed at 1020°C. I am currently experimenting with porcelain. Recent Exhibitions: Studio Ceramics V and A London 1983; Selection 84 Exhibition, Design Centre, London and Glasgow 1984; Selection 85 Exhibition, Design Centre, London and Glasgow; Crawford Centre St. Andrews, February; Playing with Fire, CPA, April; Room settings, Design Centres London and Glasgow, July to September 1985.
Collections: HRH Duke of Edinburgh, Victoria and Albert Museum, Royal Scottish Museum Edinburgh, Glasgow Museum and Art Gallery, Aberdeen Art Gallery and Museum, National Museum of Antiquities of Scotland Edinburgh; Tate Gallery, London.

Russell Coates. Initially, I studied painting and sculpture. It was during the Art Teacher Certificate course at Goldsmiths' College, London, that I started making pottery. I was particularly interested in ash glazes and reduction firing, which led eventually to some celadon and copper-red porcelain. In 1979 I was awarded the Goldsmiths' Advanced Diploma in ceramics and, from the British Council and the Japanese Government, a Mombusho Scholarship to study Kulani enamelled porcelain in Kanazawa City. This was a unique opportunity. Over a period of four years I received from a Japanese Master potter a thorough training in the techniques of blue and white porcelain and oriental enamelled porcelain: techniques which have in fact changed very little since they were imported from Ming Dynasty China. With regard to my own development as a ceramic artist, enamelling porcelain brought together my interest in painting and pottery. Working only in porcelain I make mostly large, thrown plates, thrown and handbuilt 'mountain' vases and 'rock' boxes. For decoration I use only the traditional five colour enamel palette; yellow, green, blue, violet and red, which I make myself. They are glassy semi-transparent colours of finer quality than their Western opaque counterparts. I am exploring the tremendous variety of comportions possible with combinations of these colours and the underglaze blue in geometric designs and in designs based on natural themes such as water, wind and sky.

Michael Cole. After training with Colin Pearson at Aylesford, Michael Cole moved to a farmhouse in North Wales, near Beddgelert, and has worked there, in an old barn converted to a workshop, ever since. Except for the past eighteen months when a temporary condition, affecting one hand, made work with clay inadvisable. The clay and glazes are made up from raw materials, using a red Dorset clay (RB)/Hi-plas 69 mix for the body. Glazes used are temmoku and grey matt with a variety of ash glazes, often laid one over the other. Ware is raw glazed and once fired. Firing is by oil and gas in a 21 cu.ft. downdraught kiln, likely to be superceded shortly by a small ceramic fibre gas kiln. The maturing temperature is 1260°C, with a reduced atmosphere from 1050°C, followed by forced cooling. Domestic stoneware, including mugs, teapots, casseroles, cheese dishes, bread crocks, platters and cider jars, accounts for the greater part of the production plus some sculptural pieces. Main outlets are local craft shops and a pottery showroom in the village of Nantmor in summer and all the year from the workshop. The workshop is a twenty minute walk from the nearest road.

Russell Collins. A large range of domestic stoneware produced in a double chamber, oil-fired kiln. There are also many individual pieces made, mostly large bowls and jars as well as some porcelain. A team of five people are employed and the kiln is fired weekly.

Barbara Colls attended part time pottery classes over many years at West Surrey College of Art and Design, initially under Henry Hammond, Paul Barron and his wife Penny who were all a great help in developing the bird lidded pots. Now works alone in tiny studio, mainly in oxidised stoneware and porcelain using coloured slips and glazes. Exhibitions at Guildford House, Black Horse Craft Centre Norwich and at many galleries at home and abroad.

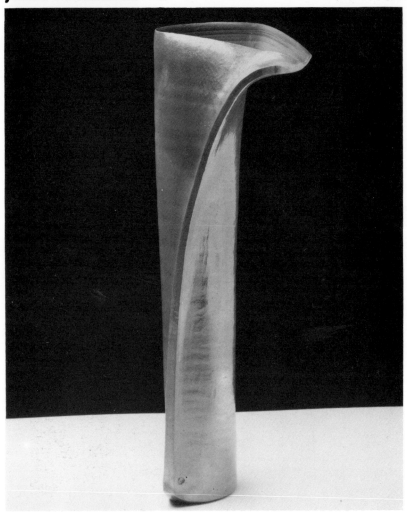

Joanna Constantinidis. Thrown and modelled pots in stoneware and porcelain. Lecturer in ceramics, Essex Institute of Higher Education, Chelmsford.

Delan Cookson

Delan Cookson. I work on my own, throwing individual bottles or container forms in porcelain, aiming for that elusive special form with its satisfying completeness that I see in museums; I have a love of historical pottery of all sorts particularly from early civilisations. Sometimes I like to work around a theme that offers more sculptural potential, breaking away from the symmetry of thrown cylindrical forms, and involving combinations of handbuilding techniques. I have repeatedly explored the contrast between hard edge and soft forms, often employing images and objects that are in themselves ambiguous. Only recently am I consciously bringing together the two aspects of my work. My present sculptural pieces all originate from thrown pots, cut and re-assembled. I like working in porcelain for its delicacy and whiteness, allowing me to use subtle coloured glazes, both oxidised and reduced. I have been potting for twenty years, learning much of my technique working for myself. Recent one-man exhibitions include: Galerie An Gross St. Martin, Cologne in 1983, and the Bohun Gallery, Henley-on-Thames in 1985. Recent mixed exhibitions include Rufford Craft Centre 'New Ceramics '82', Brunel University 'Chiltern Artists '82' Aldeburgh 'Pots and Potters Festival' 1982, Victoria and Albert Museum 'Studio Ceramics Today' 1983, Aylesbury Museum and Milton Keynes Library 1984, City Gallery, Great Linford, 'Built by Hand' 1984. Represented in public collections including Oxford County Museum, Reading Museum, Portsmouth Museum, Buckinghamshire County Council, Leicestershire Schools and Colleges Collection.

Emmanuel Cooper. Makes individual pots, mostly in porcelain, which include bowls and boxes. Glazes tend to be bright and deep – turquoise, blues and greens, uranium yellows, or smooth matts, some with chrome pink painted or stamped decoration. All are fired to 1260°C in the electric kiln. The pottery also produces a range of thrown domestic stoneware with a matt oatmeal glaze. Has been making pots for 25 years. He trained at Bournemouth School of Art, and at Hornsey School of Art, and worked with Gwyn Hanssen and then Bryan Newman before opening his own studio. His pots have been exhibited widely in this country and overseas. Major exhibitions held at the British Crafts Centre, Craftsmen Potters Shop, J.K. Hill etc. Work in many collections, including the Victoria and Albert Museum and the Royal Scottish Museum. Co-editor of *Ceramic Review*. Author of many books on ceramics including *New Ceramics* (with Eileen Lewenstein), *Glazes for the Studio Potter* (with Derek Royle) (Batsford 1978) *The Potter's Book of Glaze Recipes* (Batsford 1980), *A History of World Pottery* (Batsford 1980), *Electric Kiln Pottery* (Batsford 1982).

Suzi Cree

Suzi Cree. Born 1952, studied Studio Pottery at Harrow School of Art, and also worked as assistant to Colin Pearson, Geoffrey Eastop and Peter Dick. I design and make tableware and garden pottery in both red and white earthenware clays. I decorate using slips and glazes to build up layers of colour and surface variation, and fire in the slightly reducing atmosphere of a wood kiln. Exhibitions include group shows at CPA and British Crafts Centre and 'New Domestic Pottery' at the Crafts Council. Collections – Crafts Council. Part time lecturer ceramics and glaze theory, Harrogate College of Arts.

Dart Pottery

Dart Pottery. Dartington Pottery was founded in 1976 with the help of the Crafts Council and the Dartington Hall Trust, to provide a practical training course for students wishing to set up their own workshops. Up to the present time almost 95% of the past students are still involved in the pottery. The workshop has recently expanded and is now run (from 1984) under the name Dart Pottery as a commercial pottery by Peter Cook, Stephen Course (both former Managers) and Peter Hazell. The pottery has developed a range of domestic stoneware designed by Janice Tchalenko, which is now in production. In addition, there is a training facility offered to students. The pottery has its own shop at the Cider Press complex and supplies leading galleries and shops in the UK and abroad.
Directors — P. Cook, S. Course, P. Hazell, J. Tchalenko.

John Davidson 33

John Davidson. A comprehensive range of thrown domestic stoneware and an increasing amount of individual porcelain with applied lustre decoration. The pottery was established in 1965, following several years involving part time potting and teaching in London. Originally concerned with volume production, employing a number of assistants, but now working alone using a self-built oil fired kiln.

Clive Davies. I have been making celadon type domestic stoneware for 15 years and I feel I have completed some sort of apprenticeship considering I am self-taught. In 1981 I was in South West France for six months. During that time I set up a mini pottery firing with wood. Being in France, French pots and just being away had a profound affect on me. When I returned home and crept into my showroom I was desolate, everything looked so hard and humourless. From that point I started to change and I think improve the forms. I also developed other glazes. Early in 1983 I was staying with friends in Nottingham. They decided one day that we should visit the Yew Tree Gallery in Derbyshire to look at some embroidery work. The gallery is small, delightful and in the middle of nowhere. The embroidery was exquisite but on the tables were some pots by Sutton Taylor; amazing work swirling with rich and delicate colour. I was lifted and swore my allegiance there and then. As my mind opened I observed Janice Tchalenko's lovely work and she has given me strength, plus some recipes from *Ceramic Review*. I built a small gas kiln and fired many tests before base glazes, colour glazes and body came to a compromise. Born 1939. Self taught. Various exhibitions including Craftsmen Potters Association, Heals London, etc. Ex council member Craftsmen Potters Association. Occasional teaching Harrow and Lowestoft.

Derek Davis 36

Davis

Derek Davis. Stoneware and porcelain individual pieces thrown and hand formed, with brush drawn decoration and strong emphasis on colour and tone. Reduced and oxidised. Firing 1320-1350°C. Exhibitions include Liberty, Primavera, Amalgam, Southampton Art Gallery, Peter Dingley, Craftsmen Potters Association, Portsmouth Museum, Southover Gallery, Universities of Sussex, Southampton, Sheffield. Mixed exhibitions include Victoria and Albert Museum 1983 (catalogue cover), Primavera, Tokyo, Heidelberg, Istanbul, Frechen Germany, Kettles Yard, Boston USA, British Craft Centre, Dulwich Art Gallery, Munich (British Council). Commissions include 20' × 10' ceramic floor, London, Ford Motor Company, D.O.E., Brazilia, Rome, Warsaw, Riyadh, Barbican Art Scheme London. Collections include Victoria and Albert Museum, Garth Clark Collection USA, Paisley Museum, Keramion Frechen Germany, Prisenhof Holland, Portsmouth Museum, Southampton Museum, Contemporary Art Society, Ulster Museum Belfast. Fellowship University of Sussex 1967 — Artist in Residence, Bursary Southern Arts Association 1978, Member of International Academy of Ceramics, British Crafts Centre, Craftsmen Potters Association, Hon. Member Southern Ceramic Group, chosen by Dr. Roy Strong (Victoria and Albert Museum) with Mary Rogers for 'The Spirit of the Seventies' *Sunday Times* 1976. Ceramics shown Japanese TV NHK 2. Publications *Ceramic Review, Architectural Review, Arts Review, Southern Arts, Decorative Arts Review, New Ceramics* 1974, Contemporary Ceramics, Studio Porcelain.

Sally Dawson. Have had my own workshop in London since 1962. Am mainly self-taught after attending evening classes. Started working in earthenware but soon turned to stoneware and produced a line of oxidised domestic ware for some years. I now work solely in porcelain, producing mainly bowls, jars and teapots. Pots are of simple functional shape with minimal decoration and quiet colours, sometimes with a crackle glaze. Have done quite a lot of fluting and incising and am beginning to use some brighter colours now. Have shown at various exhibitions throughout the country including "Decorated Porcelain" exhibition at CPA in 1983. I usually work on my own and do not have need of assistants.

Peter Dick

Peter Dick. Coxwold Pottery is a small country workshop established in 1965 by Peter and Jill Dick. With the help of one assistant they make a wide range of kitchen/table-ware, planters and pots for special occasions. Most of the work is thrown, decorated with slips and fired in the large, two-chambered wood kiln giving the glazes and bodies a richly varied colour and quality. The village of Coxwold lies in an attractive part of North Yorkshire close to the city of York. Peter, who was trained by Michael Cardew and Ray Finch, also makes limited numbers of larger and more unusual pots for exhibitions and galleries. These are marked by his own initials as well as the pottery apple-tree seal.

Mike Dodd. I am building my fourth pottery, which will be partly going in 1986 and fully operational in 1987. During my rather zig-zag career as a potter I've experimented with various sorts of kilns; gas, oil, wood, oil drip and wood, and now blown oil and wood. I enjoy using local materials for slips and glazes. I find infinite subtlety in nature's offerings. In my work I like a sense of economy, of balance, of rightness which, for me, is a sense of working for usefulness, for enrichment, for Life. I just hope that people will continue to want, buy, use and experience the qualities and subtleties of good handmade pottery. I have shown work in exhibitions in Hong Kong and Germany. In this country I have contributed to many regional exhibitions and had a few notable exhibitions, for example Craftwork in 1979 Guildford, Amalgam in May 1985 London (with Jim Malone).

Jack Doherty

Jack and Joan Doherty studied at the Ulster College of Art and Design from 1966-1971 and on graduation joined Kilkenny Design Workshops as studio potters, working there until 1974. They returned to Northern Ireland to establish their first workshop in Co. Down. Two years ago they moved to live and work in Herefordshire. Their work in porcelain ranges in scale from teacups to large bowls and dishes mostly thrown with surfaces and decorations built up by inlaying coloured and textured clays. The forms are often altered by bending and cutting while the clay is still soft. Many of the stains and colours are produced in the workshop using combinations of raw oxides. They use a propane kiln fired to 1300°C with a period of light reduction from 950°C to the end of firing. Two basic glazes are used; a shiny transparent on the functional pieces, and a textured matt which produces interesting colour variations on the individual work. Pieces in various exhibitions, notably 'The Craftsmans Art' (Victoria and Albert Museum) 'International Ceramics '73' Alberta, Canada and at the exhibitions in Faenza and Vallauris where they were awarded Gold Medals in 1974 and 1976. More recently their work has been shown in group and touring exhibitions in England, West Germany, Scandanavia, and the United States and is included in the collections of The Arts Council of Northern Ireland and The Ulster Museum.

Micky Doherty

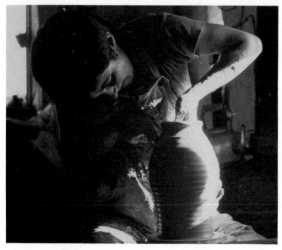

Micky Doherty. I started potting in Ireland in 1970. I attended the studio pottery course at Harrow from 1970-72. Then I worked with a saltglaze potter in France and in a traditional pottery in Spain. In 1974 I moved to Bentham on the edge of the North Yorkshire moors and set up my workshop. With the help of friends I built a 75 cu.ft. wood-fired kiln. Since then I have been making functional saltglazed tableware. During this time I have also had two children so my energy has been much divided between potting and being with the children. I have now built a smaller fast-fire kiln which I am able to fill more regularly and which also allows me to experiment more. At present I am making bowls and dishes with a poured and trailed slip decoration, as well as cut-sided bottles and a general range of tableware. The pots are all saltglazed and wood-fired. I use a variety of coloured slips. I find the wind, weather and wood all have their effect on the pots, so the results vary a lot – sometimes this can be very frustrating but it is also very exciting. I have recently started to make saltglaze tiles – some decorated, others in a plain slip; they can be used on walls or table tops etc. I am happy to make them to order.

John Dunn's raku dishes stem from a decision made five years ago to be single minded about one particular aspect of ceramics, in fact one particular form, and to eliminate all production which was not meaningful to him. Raku had always been held to be sacred and he refused to compromise in this area. In 1981 he was working on the large 23 inch diameter dish and remembers the day he vowed to devote all his energies to its exclusive development. In retrospect, he feels he should have adopted this attitude years ago, and now believes that his singlemindedness was a turning point. After five years he still derives much satisfaction from this form and is probably more involved than he has ever been. It is the maturing of the piece, the attainment of that last two or three percent which is seen as the real challenge. Glazing techniques stem from a conscious rejection of the domestic stoneware era with its greens and browns and a desire to use vibrant colour, prompted by some of the qualities in handmade glass. Exhibitions 1984 Katharine House, Marlborough, Fulham Gallery London, Goldsmiths Gallery Buckinghamshire. 1985 Bluecoat Liverpool, British Raku Rufford Notts., Craftsmen Potters Association London, Katharine House (Newbury), Ceramics 7 London, Olot Catalonia, Inter Raku '85 Spain, Museum of Ceramics Barcelona. 1986 Galerie Le Sorbier Paris.

Geoffrey Eastop

Geoffrey Eastop trained as a painter at Goldsmiths' College, London, and Academie Ranson, Paris 1949-52. Three areas of work are explored in gradual rotation to allow for the eventual application of various ideas which are noted in sketchbook form until the opportunity occurs to put them into practice. More recently much of the work has been in porcelain, a material whose tactile quality is especially suitable for pieces which are thrown and modified. Often the intention is to give a contemporary formal character to the conventional parts of the pot, lip, neck, shoulder, handle etc. The finished piece, though sometimes much altered, is still seen more as a pot than as a sculpture. Stoneware generally is approached in the same way, the difference being largely a matter of scale and character. Thrown and press-moulded dishes are usually made in earthenware using slips and glazes poured and painted. The thickness of glaze or slip giving depth and relief to the flat surface. Regular exhibitions since 1958, solo and group, including the National Museum of Wales, Cologne, Stuttgart, and Victoria and Albert Museum. Solo exhibitions 1985 at the Bohun Gallery and at Cardiff University as part of the Music Festival. Work in numerous collections include ceramic murals Maudsley Hospital, London and Reading Civic Centre. Wall and floor tiles Robinson College Chapel, Cambridge University. Reviewer for *Arts Review*. Book: *The Hollow Vessel* published by Bohun Gallery 1980.

David Edmonds trained at Goldsmiths' College, London. Set up pottery at home in 1970. Have been a part of various shows in and around London during which time my work has often related to various forms of architecture. Slab-built and stoneware fired with ash glazes or a matt-white finish. I am now in pleasant collaboration with another potter, Don Truss, and through working together we now produce ceramic gardens with indoor plants, waterways and architecture. My pottery stamp appears as a little (or several) birds on the pots.

David Eeles 45

David Eeles started making pots at Willesden School of Art in 1949. First workshop was established at Hampstead in London in 1955, moved to Dorset in 1962. Now works with family Benjamin, Simon and Caroline making mainly woodfired stoneware and porcelain. Work in many national and international private and public collections.

Derek Emms 46

Derek Emms. Born 1929, studied at Accrington, Burnley and Leeds Colleges of Art. Initially trained in textile design then became interested in pottery. On completion of National Service worked at St. Ives under Bernard and David Leach, then in 1955 became full-time lecturer at the North Staffordshire Polytechnic (formerly Stoke-on-Trent College of Art). Retired from full-time teaching in October 1985 to devote more time to producing own work. Functional and decorative pieces produced in stoneware and porcelain. All fired to 1280°C in a reducing atmosphere.

Dorothy Feibleman. Lamination is an ancient technique which transcends every artistic medium. The effects created on the surface of an article can be bold, or as subtle as a pointillist painting. The fascination of using this method in three dimensions is that the structure and decoration are integral. This technique, applied to clay, is similar to slab and coil building, but it differs by distinguishing every join with a change of colour or texture. Makes 22k and 18k gold and porcelain jewellery and porcelain and silver jewellery, as well as ceramics using laminated coloured clays. Clays used are usually coloured porcelain, parian and sanitary porcelain although some stoneware or earthenware is used for commissions. Makes ceramics full time and gives workshops and demonstrations. Many exhibitions, including the Oxford Gallery, Westminster Gallery Boston USA and Artist Potters Now.

Ray Finch. Born London 1914. Trained Central School of Arts and Crafts, London 1935 and under Michael Cardew at Winchcombe Pottery 1936-39. Took over Winchcombe Pottery in 1946 and has worked there since, producing, with a team of 4 or 5 assistants, first slipware until 1960 and then high temperature stoneware. A wide range of domestic ware is made (all wheel thrown) and fired in a large wood-fired kiln. The emphasis is and always has been, both in the standard range and in any individual pieces, on making pots which are both to be used and enjoyed. Solus Exhibitions: Opening Exhibition at Craftsmen Potters Shop, London 1960; Craftwork, Guildford 1974; Craftsmen Potters Shop, London 1979. Group Exhibitions include: International Ceramics Faenza 1970; The Craftsmens Art, Victoria & Albert Museum 1973; Aspects of Modern British Crafts, Royal Scottish Museum 1973; British Council Exhibition to Iran & Egypt 1977; British Council Exhibition to Hong Kong 1980; Crafts Council Touring Exhibition of France 1980; Crafts South West 1981; Stoke City Art Gallery 1983; Michael Cardew & Pupils 1983; Crafts Council Domestic Pottery 1984.

Robert Fournier entered the Central School of Arts and Crafts 1945/6 under Dora Billington and became technical and teaching assistant in 1947. Built and set up Ducketts Wood Pottery, Hertfordshire, 1946/7 making slipware, tin-glaze and, later, mosaics. Started the Pottery Department at Goldsmith's College 1948, stonewares, with Sheila, at potteries in Greenwich, Castle Hill in Kent and, for the last fourteen years at Lacock, Wiltshire. Part-time teaching until 1968 at Chaucer and Maidstone College of Art. Council member of the Craftsmen Potters Association for several years, organising three film festivals. Made several films with John Anderson including 'Isaac Button', 'Creatures in Clay' (Rosemary Wren), 'Raku, English style', 'David Leach' etc. and issued five hundred slides on pottery. Books include three in dictionary form *Practical Pottery, Pottery Form* with Decoration in process of publication. Also *Electric Kiln Construction* etc. Initiated and ran Craftsmen Potters Association Archives 1975-85.

Sheila Fournier trained at Goldsmiths' College, London, and has potted professionally since 1961 making stonewares, inlaid and other porcelain and some sawdust fired and raku ware. Made several hundred drawings for the books. Joint exhibitions at University of Sussex, Peter Dingley, St Albans School of Art, Bluecoat Centre, Beaux Arts (Bath) etc. The pottery at Lacock has a showroom which people are welcome to visit. No fixed hours, so please telephone if coming on a special visit. Lacock is an unspoilt village of medieval foundation owned by the National Trust and was the home of the inventor of photography, Fox-Talbot.

Sylvia Des Fours   50

Sylvia Des Fours came to England from Czechoslovakia in 1949. Trained at Epsom School of Art and Hammersmith School of Art. Makes individual pieces in reduced stoneware and porcelain: thrown or handbuilt or a combination of both. Teaches at Dorking I.O.F.E. and Richmond Adult and Community College (Special course: ''Ceramics for Therapists''), also at a psychiatric hospital in Epsom. Believes in the therapeutic value of working with clay and is deeply involved in matters of mental health.

David Frith. Stoneware and porcelain individual pieces – thrown, pressed, extruded and beaten Also full range of domestic porcelain and stoneware. Born in 1943 David trained at Flintshire and Wimbledon School of Art (1956-62) and at Stoke-on-Trent College of Art under Derek Emms (1962-3). David has been a full-time potter now since 1963, working for some years with several assistants, but since the move to the Malt House in 1975 has worked alone with his wife Margaret. His present work stems from a continual development over the years. He has never consciously made great changes in his approach, but a better understanding and feeling for the materials alongside a greater control of the skills of the making process, give him the freedom for self-expression. Thrown forms are predominant of which some are beaten or faceted, to give flat surfaces for decoration. Pressed and slabbed methods are used for the large square dishes and rectangular trays and extruded forms for the flatware and boxes. Decorative techniques include wax resist brushwork with Kaki overglaze and glaze trailing and pouring over various celadons and brushed pigments. David likes long periods of glazing and decorating with several firings close together. This way he finds he gets the maximum out of the materials, the kilns and himself. Founder member – North Wales Potters Association. Council member and current vice-chairman CPA. Full member Red Rose Guild of Designer Craftsmen.

Annette Fuchs trained at the Royal Salford Technical College School of Art and Camberwell School of Art. To gain practical experience she worked at Briglin Pottery before joining her sister at her pottery in London. In 1965 she set up her own pottery at The Old School House, Witheridge Hill, near Henley-on-Thames. She works in earthenware, stoneware and porcelain, making individual pieces and domestic ware. Fired in electric kilns. She works alone. She has exhibited several times at the Craftsmen Potters Shop, London W.1 and at Salix Windsor 1971; Seibu Stores, Tokyo, Japan 1973; Boadicea, London 1976; Pennsylvania State University Museum, USA 1976; Barclaycraft, Worthing 1979; Exhibit A, Wallingford 1980; The Smedbyn Gallery, Huskvarna, Sweden 1980; Bohun Gallery, Henley-on-Thames 1982; included in Joint Exhibition Quay Arts Centre, Southampton Art Gallery 1984; Granna Sweden 1985 and The Dower House Gallery, Berkhamsted 1985.

Tessa Fuchs. Sculptural pieces of trees, figures, landscapes and animals, decorated bowls, some practical ware, with colourful glazes both matt and glossy. The sculptural pieces are directly inspired from her own experience – gardening, walking, travelling and painting. Trained at the Royal Salford Technical College Art School and the Central School of Arts and Crafts. Works alone. Work shown in International Ceramics and The Craftsman's Art at the Victoria and Albert Museum. Recent solo exhibitions at New Ashgate Gallery, Falcon Gallery, Quay Arts Centre (Isle of Wight), Bohun Gallery (Henley-on-Thames). Teaches at Putney Art School. Featured as the potter in the BBC TV film 'In the Making' shown in 1978, 1979 and 1984. Work shown in various publications including *Studio Ceramics* by Peter Lane.

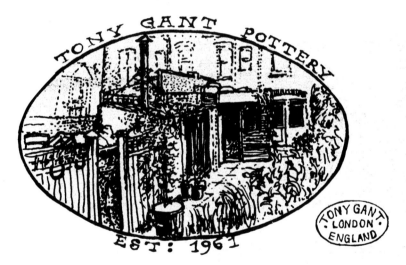

Tony Gant. Now entering its 25th year, this 'one man' studio produces a range of tableware, vases, wall tiles and plant holders in a variety of stoneware glazes. Some 10,000 pots are made each year mostly by throwing and turning. Trade enquiries are welcomed.

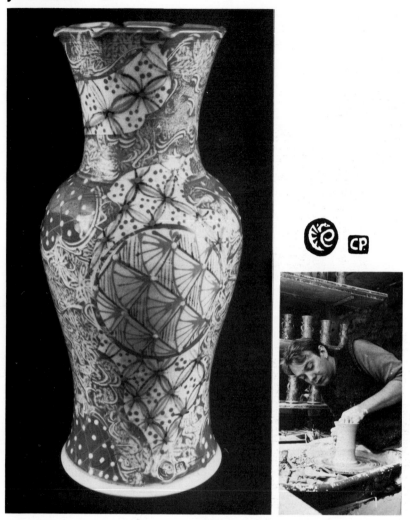

John Gibson. From 1975 to 1979 I attended the foundation and three year studio ceramics course at Chesterfield College of Art and Design. In 1977 fellow student Josie Walter and myself began to establish the courtyard pottery on the site of an old coaching inn situated in the Victorian spa town of Matlock in Derbyshire, where I began making pots after finishing my college course in 1979. Using Potclays standard porcelain body my work consists of wheel thrown forms which are made primarily as domestic tableware with a few more individually conceived pieces. All my decorative techniques are carried out at the green stage using a variety of coloured slips and underglaze colours. The work is decorated using a number of methods such as sponge stamping, sgraffito, brushwork, resist and slip training techniques. After a biscuit firing the pots are all glazed with a transparent glaze, and the final glost firing is carried out to Orton cone 8 over a period of 24 hours in an oxidising atmosphere. Work can be purchased direct from the studio and some work is sold to selected shops and galleries throughout Britain. Recent exhibitions: 1984 Bohun Gallery (one man show); David Canter Memorial Exhibition. 1985 New Members Show Craftsmen Potters Association; Shades of Blue, Craftsmen Potters Association. 1986 Porcelain at Ceramics 7. Collections: Contemporary ceramics section, Stoke-on-Trent City Art Gallery and Museum, Nottingham Castle Museum.

Ian Gregory   56

Ian Gregory was educated at Westcliff High School. His interest in the arts led him to explore work in various fine art media. However he was drawn to ceramics and after art school taught himself to throw, setting up a workshop in 1968 having moved to Dorset producing clay sculpture and stoneware domestic pottery. In 1974 the West of England Guild awarded him their Bronze and Gold Medals for his work, and in 1976 he began developing saltglaze techniques. In 1977 he was commissioned by Pitman to write a book on kiln building which is now in its second edition. In the same year he became visiting lecturer at Bath Academy of Art and Cardiff School of Art. He was also elected a member of the CPA and later elected to the Council, as well as being a founder member of the Dorset Craft Guild. He has exhibited widely both at home and abroad with many pieces in private and public collections. Work is sold through his showroom and at various galleries around the country.

Arthur J Griffiths Born 1928. First studied pottery at Wolverhampton College of Art. Went to work for Harry Davis at Crowan Pottery in Cornwall in 1949. Left there for the Werkkunstschule Darmstadt in Germany to study and make Architectural Ceramics in 1953. Returned to the U.K. to work at the Leach Pottery until 1954. Came to Loughborough College of Art to take over the Ceramics Department from David Leach, and remained in charge of the department through its change from N.D.D. to Dip A.D. and B.A. Ceramics until 1983. Since 1983 (having taken early retirement) have got back into the production of work again. Mostly individual pieces but also some functional items from garden stools downwards. All work is oil fired stoneware or porcelain. Mainly made on the wheel but large items may include slab and coil work. Exhibited widely from 1955-1975 when potting almost came to a halt, until 1983. Work is in many private and public collections.

Frank Hamer 58

Frank Hamer has been making pots and teaching pottery for over 35 years. In 1982 he retired from full-time teaching to concentrate upon potting, researching and writing with some visiting lecturing. He lives in rural Gwent, working in a studio which overlooks the Brecon Canal and sharing studio and kilns with his wife Janet. He now works exclusively in reduced stoneware making developments of decorative table pieces; commemorative pieces like goblets and loving cups; and ceramic landscape pictures. These are rectangular wall plates which use glaze effects to describe mostly Welsh locations. He is author and co-author of *Pottery Glazes, Clays, The Potter's Dictionary of Materials and Techniques* and numerous articles in publications worldwide.

Jame Hamlyn. Born 1940. Trained at Harrow, studio pottery course 1972-74. Works with husband, producing useful and decorative saltglazed stoneware and porcelain. Oil-fired kiln, 50 cu.ft., approximately ten firings a year. Does occasional workshops and teaching, main income from sale of pots. Saltglazing is a traditional technique, first developed in Germany during the fifteenth century. In England this type of ware became one of the most popular forms of pottery in the first half of the eighteenth century. Its large-scale commercial production has now almost ceased and it is only through a handful of studio potters that the tradition is being kept alive. The most distinctive feature of saltglaze is an orange-peel mottled surface. The fired surface is very bright and lively, and Jane Hamlyn's pots are often decorated with coloured slips, roulette decoration and modelled handles, exploiting the unique qualities of saltglaze. Recent exhibitions (1985): A Collection in the Making – Crafts Council London; Tableware – a New Domestic Pottery – Travelling Exhibition Crafts Council; Fast Forward – new directions in British Ceramics – Kettles Yard Gallery Cambridge. Work in public collections: Victoria and Albert Museum, London; Ulster Museum, Hanley Museum, Stoke-on-Trent; Castle Museum, Nottingham; Aberystwyth University Ceramics Collection; Sudbury Hall Collection; Crafts Council Collection; Cleveland Ceramics Collection.

Henry Hammond

ERRATA
The lidded pot on page 67 is by
Jane Hamlyn, the bowl on
page 66 is by **Henry Hammond**.
The printer apologises for this error.

Henry Hammond makes individual pieces, pots, bowls, tiles etc. in thrown and turned, decorated stoneware and porcelain. Decoration: brush drawing in oxides under matt or ash glazes: impressed seals or sgraffito. Student of the late William Staite Murray and Michael Cardew. Work in many national and international collections including Victoria and Albert Museum, London. Works alone in studio originally shared with the late Paul Barron. Occasional lectures, demonstrations and workshops undertaken.

Muriel Harris 61

Muriel Harris. Served my time with a workman thrower from a commercial pottery in 1946. For two years threw and no fire owing to postwar shortage of heat. After this set up my own workshop knowing little else. Trial and much error. My throwing easy as breathing. Years of weekly courses with Ray Marshall. When I worked alone in England Mr Lowe of Heals took all I could make. I work in glazed stoneware. I still work alone going strong at 85 years. Chiefly ash glazes. Exhibit at local gallery and Jersey Museum.

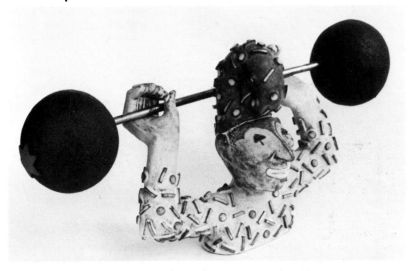

ah

Alan Heaps studied graphics under Geoffrey Wedgewood at Liverpool College of Art 1958-62.
Lectured in printmaking and analytical drawing at St. Helens School of Art until starting a ceramic
workshop near Hull in 1973, moving to mid-Wales in 1976. Fantasy is an important element in his
ceramics. Forms reflect interest in architecture, in natural and mechanical objects and in other
cultures. Sees himself primarily as a designer who uses the qualities of clay to express ideas. All
pieces are non-domestic, though the teapots can be used, if you must. The ceramics are built from
thin slabs of red clay, which are then carved, painted with coloured slips and dipped in a cream matt
glaze and fired to Orton cone 01. The majority of his ceramics are sold through European galleries.
Exhibitions include Rochdale Art Gallery 1975; Boadicea, London 1976; Art and Ceramic Gallery,
Richmond, Ferens Civic Gallery, Hull 1977; Graphik Kabinett, Darmstadt 1978; Werkhof Bissendorf,
Hannover 1980 and 1983; Wales Art Council, Cardiff and Mold, Mottenburger Gallery, Hamburg
1982; Goldene Nudel Galerie, Ober-Ramstadt, 1985.

Ewen Henderson. Assemblages of differing clays, i.e. stoneware and porcelain coloured with oxides and stains put together in various ways so that the decoration and the pot are the same thing. Motifs used vary from stripes to spirals which after putting together are manipulated into forms relating as naturally as can to the decoration. All are oxidised stoneware covered with simple wood ash or Shino-type glazes mostly applied in raw state by brushing or similar methods.

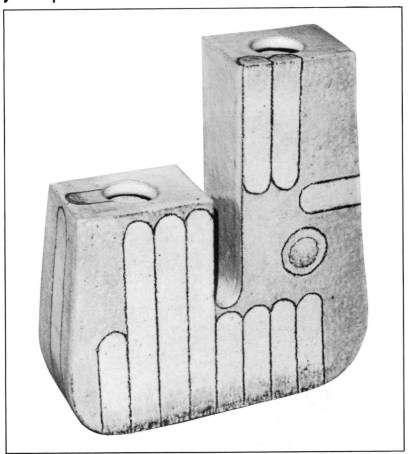

J. Hepworth

Joan Hepworth studied at Hastings School of Art for two years. While there won a scholarship to the Royal College of Art and entered the Design School to study mural decoration, fabric design and printing. After leaving college spent a year in a film cartoon studio before taking up teaching design and printing at Sutton School of Art. When pottery was introduced into the school she joined a class in her spare time and was taught by Harry Stringer and Brian Starkey. She became more and more enthusiastic over pottery and experimented with all methods of making pots. Eventually bought her own kiln and wheel and set up her own workshop. Finding she used the wheel less and less she decided after moving to her present address, to concentrate on slab pots and slip cast porcelain. Enjoys exploring and developing new shapes. Decorates mainly with ceramic crayons and some relief work. Uses an electric kiln firing to 1250°C. Finds the coloured crayons fade at higher temperatures. Has exhibited widely in this country with one person exhibitions at Sutton School of Art and at Henley. Has also exhibited in Belgium, Austria and West Germany and sold to Japan.

Anita Hoy 66

Anita Hoy. Mainly individual pieces, earthenware, stoneware, porcelain and some raku. Working alone. Trained at Copenhagen College of Art. Started and became head of studio departments at Bullers Ltd., Stoke-on-Trent, and Royal Doulton at Lambeth, working with porcelain and saltglazed stoneware. Looking for oneness of form and decoration, comprising: carving, coloured slips and oxide brushwork, under or over clear and opaque coloured reduction fired glazes at 1260°C. Work illustrated in books and articles (*Doulton Lambeth Wares* by D Eyles 1976 and *Studio Porcelain* by Peter Lane 1980). Retrospective Bullers exhibition at Gladstone Pottery Museum 1978 and Doulton Story at Victoria and Albert Museum 1979. Represented with a collection at Victoria and Albert Museum, and City Museum, Stoke-on-Trent. Taught for many years at West Surrey Colleges of Art and Design; at present teaching at Richmond Adult College.

John Huggins makes, with the help of two assistants, a range of terracotta plant pots. They range from small pots for window sills to large feature pots for gardens and patios. Many of his pots are decorated with a motif of the life-giving forces — the sun and the rain. He uses a local clay and fires with oil.

Neil Ions. Born in Newcastle-under-Lyme, Staffordshire 1949. Foundation training at Newcastle School of Art, Staffordshire. Dip.A.D. Newport College of Art, Gwent 1969-72. M.A. Royal College of Art, London 1972-75. Founder member of Fosseway House Workshops, Stow-on-the-Wold, Glos. November 1975. Member Gloucestershire Guild of Craftsmen. Work in the Victoria and Albert Collection. Maker of musical objects, instruments and sculpture. Ocarinas in a variety of bird forms, a range of single and multiple flutes and sculptural pieces, mostly slabbed which often have a musical component. The work is entirely earthenware, using press-moulding, coiling, slabbing and free modelling techniques, painted with a wide range of earthenware slips. The surface is lightly burnished before firing to 1080°C in an oxidised atmosphere. Wax polish is applied after firing. The nature of the work results from a fusion of interests in the natural world, music and American Indian artefacts. Member of Friends of the Earth. Exhibitions at Craftsmen Potters Shop: Jugs 'New Members Show', new work 'People and other animals'.

John Jelfs   69

John Jelfs. Interest in pottery first aroused in Bombay whilst working as an engineer by seeing an old man throwing 2 foot sections of drainpipe with great precision on an old kick-wheel. Left engineering to train as a potter at Cheltenham School of Art. Worked at Hook Norton Pottery for Russell Collins. Set up present workshop in the busy Cotswold village of Bourton-on-the-Water in 1972 with wife Judy making tinglaze and slip earthenware. Changed to oil-fired stoneware production in 1976. Various exhibitions in U.K. 2 pieces included in Studio Ceramics Today, Victoria and Albert Museum 1983. Work sold direct from the studio and a number of galleries. Production now mainly domestic stoneware with an ever-increasing number of one-offs and porcelain pieces. Regret no places for students in the foreseeable future.

Christopher Jenkins 70

Christopher Jenkins. Prefers working in oxidised stoneware and at present produces a variety of decorated individual pieces. Trained as a painter at the Slade School and as a potter at the Central School, London. Senior lecturer in ceramics at Manchester Polytechnic.

David Lloyd Jones. I began making pots in 1962 when I was 34. I work in stoneware and porcelain and make a wide variety of vessels, most of which are useful in some way. I enjoy going up in scale making large pots and lidded jars up to 3ft. high and plates and bowls to about 20 ins. diameter. I am primarily interested in form but do decorate the majority of pots, usually with glaze on glaze applied with a brush or slip trailer. Sometimes a wax decoration is used between the glaze layers. The kiln is oil fired and has a capacity of 125 cubic feet and was built in 1972. This is glaze fired about every two months. I also have a small wood kiln, 25 cubic feet capacity, the design based on the American potter, Jerry William's Phoenix kiln. A small wood fired saltglaze kiln has been built, with Ruth King who uses my workshop. For further information see article by W.A. Ismay, *Ceramic Review 87*, 1984. Work in the following public collections: Victoria and Albert Museum, London; Fitzwilliam Museum, Cambridge; Liverpool Museum; Kunstindustrimuseum, Bergen; Glasgow Museum; Crafts Council; Ulster Museum, Belfast; Stoke-on-Trent Museum; Belgian State Collection, Brussels; Huddersfield Art Gallery; Wurtembergisches Landmuseum, Stuttgart.

Walter Keeler. Functional pottery of an individual nature in saltglazed stoneware.

Colin Kellam 73

 K.

Colin Kellam, born in 1942, studied sculpture as well as pottery at the Loughborough College of Art. His education in the craft was furthered by working for six years under the supervision of Marianne de Trey at Shinners Bridge Pottery near Totnes. He started his own business in 1969, converting the Lion Brewery in Totnes and, particularly, building an oil-burning kiln capable of firing large items. All his work is in stoneware – fired at temperatures around 1300°C. Apart from a range of domestic ware decorated with a variety of floral motifs, the pottery produces larger items such as planters, lamp-bases and umbrella stands. Much of the floral decorating is done by Anne Beaty, his 'number one' assistant. Colin also makes good use of his early training in sculpture and enjoys creating large pieces, both decorative and useful, that are as unusual in conception as they are a pleasure to behold.

Danny Killick   74

Danny Killick trained at Walthamstow School of Art and Harrow School of Art and Design. Established first workshop in 1970. Recently moved to present address and now engaged in setting up new studio, workshop and showroom. Makes a small range of high fired, thrown functional ware. Has exhibited at Craftsmen Potters Association, Bohun Gallery, Crafts Council Touring Exhibitions, various group shows in England and Europe. Currently Course Director, Studio Pottery, Harrow School of Art.

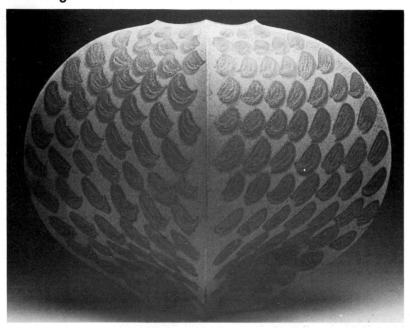

Ruth King trained at Camberwell School of Art and Crafts 1973-1977, and then started work on her own in a workshop in London. In 1981 she moved to York where she now lives and has her own studio. Her pots are hand-built in stoneware clay using various techniques of construction. Two or three glazes are sprayed on for variation in both colour and surface quality, with additional glaze-on-glaze decoration on some pieces. Until now all the pots have been fired in a six cubic foot electric kiln, but she is currently experimenting with saltglaze and is building a wood-fired kiln for this purpose. Recently her work has been seen in exhibitions which include '8 × 8 Ceramicists' at the British Crafts Centre, London, and 'Studio Ceramics Today' at the Victoria and Albert Museum, both in 1983, and 'The Individual Eye' at the Craftsmen Potters Association and is on the Selected Index of the Crafts Council. Work has been purchased by the Victoria and Albert Museum, the Ulster Museum in Belfast, the Leicester Museum and the York City Art Gallery.

Peter Lane 76

Peter Lane

Peter Lane. Trained at Bath Academy of Art. Currently teaching part-time as Senior Fellow in Ceramics at the University of East Anglia, Norwich. He is a Fellow of the Society of Designer-Craftsmen and was awarded the Society's Silver Medal in 1981. Author of *Studio Porcelain* (Pitman 1980), *Studio Ceramics (Collins 1983), and many articles in Ceramic Review, Crafts* magazine, etc. His next book, *Explorations in Ceramic Form*, will be published by Collins in 1987. Widely exhibited in Britain, Europe, Australia and North America. Represented in many private and public collections around the world. He has also given lectures and demonstrations extensively in Britain, Australia and the United States. Major stimulus derives from landscape, or forms and patterns found in nature. Various kinds of symmetry and a sense of order akin to much of natural design are important elements in the individual pieces he makes. Rarely working from drawings, he prefers to develop ideas and feelings for subject matter directly in clay, where his response to, and control (or otherwise) of, the materials and processes inevitably leads to adjustments in concept as the work proceeds. Most work is in porcelain, especially translucent bowls springing from narrow footrings. Carved, incised or pierced rims and walls are distinctive features. His love of mountains led to carving 'horizons' around the rims of bowls, some being clearly recognizable as hills and trees while others are less obvious although derived from the same source.

Richard Launder. At present my work is involved in exploring and expanding an area which is concerned with both functional and abstract concepts. Making in series of variations on a theme/continuous development/reappraisal; to and fro; from a functional focus to a point where their relation to function is symbolic/metaphoric; and back again. Technically I am working with, and extending the boundaries of high temperature saltglaze (1300°C); to understand and use the variety (of colour/texture/depth/structure) possible within a purposefully limited range of clays, slips, glazes. Where one slip can be white-red-orange-tan-brown/green-black; matt-silky-glossy. This spectrum is made possible by a thorough application of experience gained – choice/use of materials, kiln management. The kiln used as a creative tool to realize the full potentials of these materials – variety within limitations. Studied ceramics at West Surrey College of Art and Design, Farnham, Surrey (1972-76). Has worked and exhibited widely in England, Greece and Norway, both as potter and lecturer; and is represented in a number of private and museum/college public collections. Member of Northern Potters Association. Major exhibitions: 'Contemporary British Pottery' British Council, Hong Kong 1980; 'Five English Potters' Gallerie N.K. Bergen, Norway, 1982; 'Selling Saltglaze' Craft Study Centre, Bath 1983; 'New Members' Craftsmen Potters Shop, London; 'Solo' Aberystwyth Arts Centre, Mid-Wales University; 'Saltglaze' 2-Person Aphi Gallery, Athens, Greece, 1984.

David Leach started in 1930 with father, Bernard Leach, as student, manager and partner at the Leach Pottery, St. Ives until 1956. Now after 55 years potting works alone on thrown stoneware and porcelain, mostly commissions and individual pots. Prices range from £5 to £300. Exhibits regularly in the United Kingdom, USA, Japan and the Continent in group or one man shows. Work in many national and continental museums. Past chairman of the Craftsmen Potters Association and council member of the Crafts Council. Late external assessor for studio pottery courses Harrow School of Art, Scottish Education Department and other colleges of art. Initiated Dartington Pottery Training Workshop 1975 with the late David Canter. Gold Medallist Istanbul 1967. One time Head Ceramics Department Loughborough College of Art 1953-54. Spends part of each year giving lectures, demonstrations, workshops chiefly in USA, Canada and on the Continent.

Janet Leach was born in Texas USA 1918. Moved to New York to study sculpture. Began studying pottery in 1948. Met Bernard Leach, Shoji Hamada and Soetsu Yanagi at a two weeks seminar at Black Mountain College, North Carolina in 1952. Began negotiations to study under Hamada in Japan and was accepted 1954-5. In 1956 came to England to marry Bernard Leach and became a partner, her duties included the daily management of the pottery. She made her own pots usually in the evenings and weekends. Bernard Leach died in 1979 and no more standard wares made. Now works daily throwing her own individual pots. Likes using several different clays and firing techniques – all reduction stoneware. She continues to exhibit widely, including bi-annual exhibitions in Japan. She had a number of one-person exhibitions and her work was included in many national and international shows and collections.

John Leach   80

John Leach's reputation as a potter is founded on the highly successful "Muchelney" woodfired domestic stoneware which was evolved at his Somerset pottery over 21 years. The familiar hand thrown standard range with its robust, rounded shapes and distinctive flamed finish, is to be found not only in kitchens throughout Britain but worldwide in exhibitions and museums of contemporary ceramics. In 1983 John Leach expanded his creative outlook, following in the footsteps of his father David and grandfather Bernard Leach in experimenting with new shapes and inspirations. His arresting Black Pots are one result of this new, individual diversification. His fascination with the fiery unpredictability of his Japanese-style kiln remains total. Born Pottery Cottage, St. Ives Cornwall 1939, apprenticed (1957) to Bernard and David Leach. Trained also with Ray Finch and Colin Pearson. Set up Californian Pottery and taught in USA 1963. Established Muchelney Pottery, making oil-fired stoneware 1964. Work in 'Craftsman's Art' (Victoria and Albert Museum) 1976. Work in 'Makers Eye' (Crafts Council) 1982, J K Hill London, 1984.

Eileen Lewenstein

Eileen Lewenstein makes individual pots and objects in stoneware and porcelain, including thrown porcelain bottles, press-moulded stoneware dishes and most recently modular sculptures based on breakwater forms and stoneware panels in which objects found on the beach are embedded and fired. Has been potting for 40 years, mostly in London until moving to Hove and setting up her studio on the beach, in 1976. The sea and its effect on the shore plays an increasingly important part in her work. Exhibited widely in this country and abroad including USA 1983, 1985; New Zealand 1983; Yugoslavia 1984, 1985. Represented in many public and private collections including Victoria and Albert Museum; Glasgow Art Gallery and Museum; Museum of Decorative Arts, Prague; Museum of Contemporary Ceramics, Bechyne, Czechoslovakia; Villeroy and Boch Sculpture Park, Mettlach, West Germany; Auckland Institute and Hawkes Bay Art Gallery and Museum, New Zealand. Co-Editor *Ceramic Review*. Co-Editor with Emmanuel Cooper *New Ceramics* Studio Vista 1974.

John Lomas. Thrown domestic stoneware and individual pots in stoneware and porcelain, reduction fired. Also terracotta and stoneware garden pots made occasionally. Self taught and works alone. Part time lecturer in ceramics at Langley College, Berks. and Amersham College, Bucks. Has had exhibitions at Windsor; Henley-on-Thames; Lewes, Sussex; Cookham, Berks. and Chalfont St Giles, Bucks.

Andrew McGarva known in the past as a bigware thrower and saltglazer, has exhibited widely at home and abroad. His workshop, established in 1979, is at Wobage Farm, where Michael and Sheila Casson also work. He makes raw fired colourful painted useful pots. They range from mugs to large punch bowls, and are woodfired to stoneware temperature. He also produces a range of gas fired blue and white tiles. These, like the pots, are often decorated with farm animals and still-life subjects.

Mal Magson

Mal Magson works alone in small home studio producing individual pieces of unglazed handbuilt stoneware. Trained at Loughborough College of Art and Design. 1968/72 developing the process used to produce her personal style of agateware. A combination of porcelain and clay coloured with body-stains and oxides is laminated, then repeatedly rolled and folded to produce decorative slabs. These slabs are further cut and rolled and used to produce mainly bowl forms from simple press moulds. Exhibiting on average six times a year and supplying galleries with stock. Work in public and private collections throughout Britain, Europe and America.

M A L T o Y

John Maltby. Individual pieces in stoneware; some with enamel decoration. Recent pots are usually oxidised with coloured glaze decoration. These are fired in a propane kiln. Major one-man exhibitions include: Amalgam Art, London; British Crafts Centre, London; Craftsmen Potters Association, London; Beaux Arts, Bath; Peter Dingley Gallery, Stratford; Parnham House, Dorset; Gallery La Maine, Brussels, Belgium; Kyoto Museum, Japan and Darlington Hall, England. Other major exhibitions: International Exhibition of Ceramics Victoria and Albert Museum, London; International Exhibition of Ceramics Faenza, Italy (Gold Medal); Museum of Modern Ceramics Deidesheim, Germany and Kettles Yard, Cambridge. Pots are included in national and international collections including Victoria and Albert Museum, Crafts Council Collection, Firenza International Collection, University of North Wales collection, Leicester Museum, Exeter Museum, Glasgow Museum, etc.

Victor Margrie

Victor Margrie. Setting up new workshop in Bristol January 1986. Trained at Hornsey College of Art (now Middlesex Polytechnic). Former Course Director, Harrow Studio Pottery Course. Director of the Crafts Council 1971-1984. Fellow of the Society of Industrial Artists and Designers. Appointed CBE 1984.

Leo Francis Matthews

Leo Francis Matthews studied graphics at Manchester College of Art and ceramics at Stoke-on-Trent College of Art. Lectured on ceramics for over twenty-four years at various major Colleges of Art in Britain. Produces sculptural ceramics, murals and some domestic studio pottery.

Peter Meanley 89

pm85

Peter Meanley. Bowls have been a primary concern for several years. I try to achieve a harmony and continuity of form through the juxtaposition of different (primarily wheel formed) elements. Latterly I have been deliberately retaining some of the process forming marks to instill life (or introducing these artificially by means of ribs or profiles as appropriate). Handles, either real or symbolic, are very important as they provide a focal point and the opportunity for richness and change. The foot and rim, as termination points, are critical as is the continuity of inside and outside. Decoration is important and the suggestion of 3D space has been variously explored by painting semi-vitreous slips within inscribed repeat perspective progressions. Initially I produce copious ranges of 'bits' for subsequent re-assembly and normally have up to three pieces under consideration at one time. I turn and re-build extensively. After a 1030°C biscuit, I harden on the glaze to 1110°C preparatory to the painting of slips and the final 1180°C oxidised firing. I have exhibited widely, undertaken commissions, been a member of various working parties, am an experienced assessor, though my main love is making bowls.

Eric James Mellon

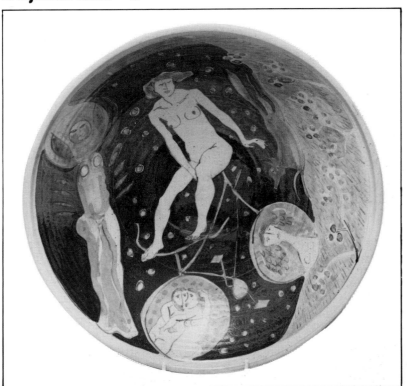

Eric James Mellon, born Watford 1925, studied at Watford, Harrow and Central School of Arts and Crafts London. Makes stoneware pots fired to 1300°C, using tree and shrub ash glazes, brush drawn decoration; oxidised and reduction firing. 1984 name added to the list of craftsmen whose work is sought by the Crafts Study Centre, Holburne Museum, Bath. Major exhibitions include Guildford House Gallery, Surrey and Abbot Hall Art Gallery, Kendal 1969; Commonwealth Institute, London 1973; Portsmouth Museum 1974; Arts Centre, Folkestone 1975 and 1983; David Paul Gallery, Chichester 1978; Westminster Gallery, Boston, USA 1981; Katharine House Gallery, Marlborough 1982; Paul Rice Gallery, London 1984; New Ashgate Gallery, Farnham, Surrey and Easton Rooms, Rye, Sussex 1985. Events: Guest Speaker Cork Potters Association 1980. Lecture Boston USA 1981. Workshop Leader, International Symposium Ireland 1982. Work represented widely in collections in Britain and internationally; purchased by Victoria and Albert Museum 1984.

D. M.

David Miller. Present work consists of thrown and handbuilt individual pieces. Surface treatment obtained by using combinations of coloured slips, glazes and brushwork. The pots are fired at low temperature in a copper saturated salt vapour. Salt is used at low temperature i.e. 950-1000°C not as a glazing agent but more as a catalyst to draw out subtle nuances of colour inherent to the clay body and the coloured slips. The technique can give rich and subtle colour variations and in order to obtain these effects, the atmosphere within the kiln must be carefully controlled so as to maintain a neutral flame. Ideally, a blue smokeless flame should be established as soon as possible, usually when the pyro is reading between 700-800°C and about midway through the 3-4 hour firing schedule. Exhibitions in England, France and Germany.

David Morris 92

David Morris attended Leeds College of Art in the late 1950s flirting with Interior Design and Fine Art before settling on Furniture Design for the National Diploma in Design and Cabinet Making for the City and Guilds. A trial session on the potter's wheel at the end of that course was the beginning of an interest in the craft. Started teaching in Hull where attendance at the College of Art led to a second N.D.D. in pottery. Began teaching at Grimsby School of Art in 1962 and gradually developed the first workshop in Laceby. Became a member of the Craftsmen Potters Association in 1979 and gave up full-time teaching to have more time to develop his own work. Started making ware with blue decoration (sponged and brushed) under a grey white glaze. The main sources of influence have been Sung, Tzu-chou, Oribe and the painted pottery of Islam. His pots for the last 15 years have been fired in electric kilns and have been almost exclusively one clay, one glaze and one decorative material and method. Recently, a 16 cu.ft. propane kiln has been constructed which enables other processes to be used. Exhibitions 1983-85 at York, Manchester, Lincoln, Sutton, London and Derbyshire, Beverley, Milton Keynes.

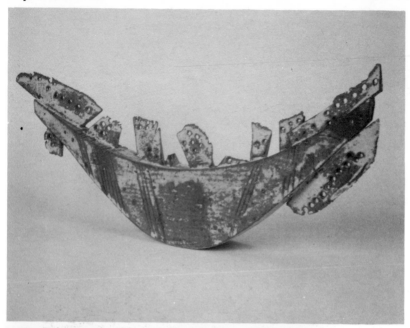

Bryan Newman. I studied at the Camberwell School of Art and Crafts where two important things happened to me. (I) I discovered pottery and (2) I met Julie. Six joyful years were spent in this sheltered environment. After ten turbulent years in London: a tangle of odd jobs, technical assisting, part-time teaching, sharing a workshop with four friends, marriage and children, we had gathered just about enough banknotes together to move west and discover Somerset (1965). We converted the tumbledown outbuildings of Hall's Farm into Aller Pottery. In the first year we nearly went bankrupt several times but managed to hang on until fortune smiled on our efforts. Since then we have steadily civilized the buildings, the garden and the pottery (not too much). The ceramic sculpture started accidentally in 1961 when I cut up a leatherhard bottle and idly played around with the pieces; it turned itself into a cactus. Since then thrown shapes cut up and slabs have turned into a whole range of boats, buildings, housescapes, industrial complexes and bridges. I have always enjoyed making thrown pots (from egg cups to bread-crocks) but much to my surprise we have become "The local potter", though we still sell to about a dozen shops and have one or two exhibitions a year. We make oil fired reduced stoneware 1280–1300°C. The prices range from £2–£100.

Eileen Nisbet

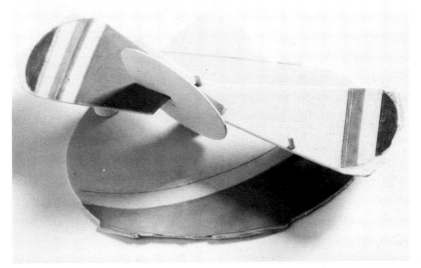

Eileen Nisbet. Using porcelain or white firing clay I aim to work with the same freedom of idea, form, line, colour, movement of a graphic artist or painter. The sculptures are sometimes about man-made objects, or plant forms. Free-standing they are inlaid and painted with slips and enamels and fired to 1250°C. Exhibited mainly in London and America.

Odundo
1985

Magdalene Anyango N Odundo was born in Nairobi, Kenya. Went to school in New Delhi, India and in Kenya. Trained and worked in commercial art and advertising in Kenya from 1969 to 1971. Cambridge Art College — Foundation and Graphics (1971-73). West Surrey College of Art and Design (1973-76). Royal College of Art (1979-1982). Taught at the Commonwealth Institute London 1976-1979. Makes handbuilt ceramics.

Warwick Parker

Warwick Parker produces mainly handthrown stoneware using a wide range of decorative treatments, including resist, stencilling, slip and glaze trailing, glaze on glaze, brushwork, pierced and raised decoration. Work is centred around individual pieces, or domestic articles of an individual nature, but a wide range of solely domestic ware is available. Various commemorative work is undertaken or other commissions accepted. Firings are done either in a large oil fired kiln or a smaller propane kiln. Trained as a thrower at the Poole Pottery, attended Poole School of Art, worked for David Leach for three and a half years. Exhibitions include Primavera and Kettles Yard, Cambridge; Westward TV Open Art Exhibitions; Fletcher Brownbuilt, New Zealand; Wolverhampton Art Gallery; Wessex Potters, Winchester; Studio Ceramics Today at the Victoria and Albert Museum. Exhibited in Germany in Hamburg, Stuttgart and Sandhavsen, mixed exhibition at Barclaycraft Gallery, Group exhibitions at the Craftsmen Potters Association. Has been a member of the Craftsmen Potters Association since 1967. Lectured or taught in various colleges.

Colin Pearson makes individual pieces in porcelain and stoneware. Trained in painting at Goldsmiths' College. Worked under Ray Finch and David Leach. Exhibits widely in UK and abroad. 1975 winner of 33rd Premio Faenza. Part-time teaching at Camberwell and Medway College of Design.

Anthony Phillips 98

Anthony Phillips. Trained at Harrow College of Higher Education, 1978-80. Since 1981 has had a studio in a riverside warehouse in Wapping, London. Makes a wide range of domestic pottery from mugs to casseroles, plates to cheese dishes and individual items like bowls and platters. There are currently four different colour ranges based on different background colours – white, blue, grey or green – with a strong, vigorous decoration on top in various combinations of colours which include yellow, pink, blue, green and black. All work is thrown and hand-decorated using slip-trailing – a traditional European technique. Two kinds of clay are used, a red earthenware (terracotta) and a white earthenware. The background colour and slip decoration are applied at the raw stage with a clear shiny glaze over. Most work is sold to shops and galleries in Britain and abroad but commissions and direct sales from the workshop are welcome by appointment. "I like throwing and slip-trailing because they are techniques that make it easy to change and evolve shapes and designs. My pottery is meant to be used but I also want it to be visually pleasing and challenging".

Peter Phillips. Trained at Wimbledon School of Art and the Royal College of Art. He is a full time teacher in charge of the ceramics course at Medway College of Design, but makes time to produce pots in a studio attached to his house in the village of Trottiscliffe (pronounced Trosley). He works with his wife Julie making mainly stoneware boxes in the form of boats and houses decorated with trees, landscapes, birds, sunbursts, and plant forms etc. He also enjoys throwing, making casseroles, jugs, plant holders etc. These are fired in a 12 cu.ft. gas kiln to cone 9. The boxes are glazed in slip glazes stained with oxides and he gains much variation by altering the thickness. Peter and Julie also have a studio in France (Dordogne) with an oil fired kiln which he built himself with the help of friends. They work there for several weeks a year producing a similar range of work but using local materials. They sell their work in various galleries in the U.K. and on the Continent. Major recent exhibitions: Contemporary British Pottery, Hong Kong Arts Centre 1980; Figuratieve Kerameik De Rozengalerie, Amsterdam 1981; Trio Winding Street Gallery, Hastings 1981.

Henry Pim first trained as a teacher, and after completing the course at Brighton College of Education in 1969 he travelled abroad for two years before taking up teaching in two London primary schools for four years. During this time he went to evening classes at Morley College and Goldsmiths' College, London. In 1974 he decided to give up his job and was able to go to Camberwell School of Art and Crafts, London, from whence he graduated in 1979 with a B.A. in ceramics. Henry starts to make his pot or bowl forms by producing paper templates or maquettes which are then dismantled and used like a dressmaker's pattern to cut out the textured slabs of clay from which the pieces are built. The pieces are surfaced with multiple layers of slip, engobe and glaze. He has exhibited widely in England, Europe and America and is represented in London by Anatol Orient (28 Shelton Street, Covent Garden, London WC2).

Ian Pirie trained in ceramics and sculpture at Grays School of Art, Aberdeen 1969-73, with a post-graduate year in ceramics. Joined Bill Brown at Rosebank Pottery, forming a partnership which originally produced tableware (highly fired stoneware in a reduction kiln to 1280°C). In 1979 helped set up and establish a craft workshop in the grounds of Crathes Castle (National Trust) and since 1980 has been lecturing full-time at Grays School of Art. "I have retained my liking for high temperature ceramics, which still feature in my work. During my time at Rosebank I developed individual work, mainly wheel thrown pieces in porcelain, decorated with oxides using an air brush. The work at this time contained very naturalistic imagery and although it is possibly less obvious, my current work still draws its inspiration from landscape. I enjoy experimenting with the relationships of two-dimensional imagery on the wheel thrown three-dimensional form, relating geometry with asymmetry. Having been a production thrower, I find that the wheel is the most natural means of expression for me, and have never felt limited by it. Currently I am working with white stoneware throwing clay. A number of pieces also incorporate porcelain elements and are fired in either oxidation or reduction kilns." Exhibited widely both in Britain and abroad. Major recent exhibitions: The Henderson Gallery, Edinburgh 1980; Booth House Gallery, Huddersfield 1980; Craftsmen Potters Shop, London 1981; Craftsmen in Scotland: touring exhibition organised by the British Crafts Centre 1982; Mainly Porcelain, The Chestnut Gallery, Bourton-on-the-Water, Gloucestershire 1983; Studio Ceramics Today, Victoria and Albert Museum, London 1983. Work in Collections: National Museum of Wales, Cardiff; Scottish National Museum, Edinburgh; Paisley Museum and Art Gallery; Scottish Crafts Collection, Edinburgh; Fremantle Arts Centre, Western Australia.

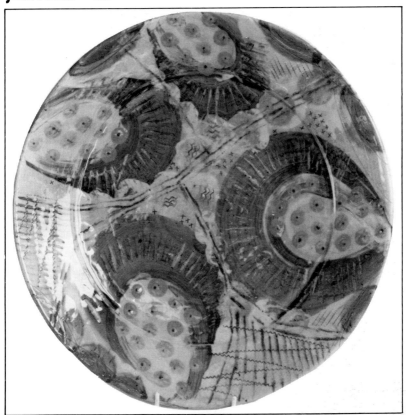

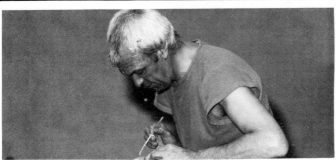

John Pollex trained at Harrow College of Art 1968-70. Assistant to Bryan Newman and Colin Pearson 1970-71. Present workshop established November 1971. Author of *Slipware* (Pitmans 1979). Major recent exhibitions Ceramics 84, Rufford Craft Centre Nottingham, Ceramics Spectacular Plymouth Art Centre, Devon 1984. My work is made with a red earthenware body and glaze fired to 1100°C in an electric kiln. From 1971-1984 the work was mainly inspired by the decoration of the seventeenth century Staffordshire slipware potters, in particular Thomas Toft. During 1984 I developed a range of coloured slips which I use under a clear glaze; the slips are applied to the work with a variety of brushes. I also incorporate trailing, sgraffito and various stamps as part of the decoration. I am now in the process of phasing out the old slipware in favour of the ''new-deco'' ware. I will continue to produce commemorative slipware dishes to order.

Vicki Read started her pottery in Winslow, North Buckinghamshire in 1962 after helping and teaching in evening classes for eight years. She is a founder member of the CPA, i.e. some 25 years. Mainly taught through experience, I work in stoneware reduction fired in a natural gas fired kiln. I am still evolving and developing the forms which I enjoyed making in the beginning, i.e. large bowls, platters and long necked pots of all sizes up to patio size 36" high. Range of domestic ware also made. I still use a "Block Design" under various glazes. This year the colours are gayer, i.e. reds and blues, with greens, along with the softer stoneware colours. Now that the family are more independent I am working full-time again.

Stanislas Reychan. Modelled figures and ornaments. Born 1897. Trained at St. Martin's School of Art and Central School of Arts and Crafts under Dora Billington. Has exhibited at the R.A. Design Centre and has had many one-man shows. Paris Salon Bronze Medal 1958, Silver Medal 1960. M.B.E.

Mary Rich worked with David Leach and Harry and May Davis in early 1960s. Started own workshop 1962 with gas fired salt kiln. Moved in 1970 to present address – kiln now oil fired saltglaze, and all pots once fired. Mostly domestic stoneware at this time. Stoneware gradually phased out as preference for white bodies and porcelain evolved. In 1983 acquired 4 cu.ft. propane ceramic fibre kiln, since when all work has been in porcelain and is totally concerned with the decorative qualities of gold and other metals combined with coloured on glaze lustres. My interest in saltglazing has temporarily been put to one side although I do still have an oil fired salt kiln. I do not employ assistants. Exhibitions in 1985 include The English Gallery, Geisenheim, Germany; The Martha Schneider Gallery, Illinois, USA; The Westminster Gallery, Boston, USA; The Chestnut Gallery, Bourton-on-the-Water, Gloucestershire; Primavera, Cambridge; Craftsmen Potters Association, 'Shades of Blue'; Free Hand Gallery, Los Angeles, USA; J. K. Hill, London.

CAR / car

Christine-Ann Richards studied Studio Pottery Course at Harrow School of Art & Technology (1970-73). Works alone. Uses porcelain to make boxes, bowls, vases, lidded jars as well as larger more individual pieces. "In the 1970s I concentrated on making smaller pots where I used a matt-white flecked glaze to which I added colouring oxides. These were fired in an oxidising atmosphere to 1280°C. With the prompting of a solo exhibition in 1980 and the idea of making larger pots I decided to develop a new range of glazes. The CPA trip to China in 1978 made me aware of the different types of crackle glazes used in earlier dynasties. As well as using the transparent glaze which I left plain or stained with Chinese ink, I developed thick crackle glazes in opaque white, pink, blue and yellow. In 1984 I spent four months travelling in China and was very much excited by modern Chinese paintings. Some of my recent work with copper red and green splash decoration across the white surface of the pot are reminiscent of the paintings that I saw." Work in public and private collections. Exhibitions in England and abroad.

David Roberts

David Roberts. produces a range of large decorative raku fired vessels. All the pots are coil built and exhibit a concern with simplicity of form and emphasis on interior space and volume, together with a fascination with and control over surface incident arising from firing and reduction processes. The work has been exhibited widely throughout the UK and abroad, and is represented in many private and public collections including the Victoria and Albert Museum, Ulster Museum and the Museum of Wales.

James W Robison

James W Robison. American background in ceramics and sculpture. M.A. Eastern Michigan University. Established Yorkshire workshop and gallery in 1975. Lectures at Bretton Hall College, Wakefield. Large scale pieces combine moulding and handbuilding techniques to make sculpture and individual pieces. Influences include standing stones, fossils, ageing processes and geometric configurations. Colour is an important feature and pastel hues of blue, cream and yellow contrast rust reds and darker shades in each piece. Architectural and individual commissions are undertaken. Stoneware firing render work suitable for gardens and exterior sites as well as domestic and other interior locations. Recent commissioned works include sculptured columns for the Grafton Centre, Cambridge (one of four pictured above) and an exterior relief sculpture as part of new development called Salters Row in Pontefract. Exhibits regularly and works are in collections throughout the United Kingdom and in America.

MER

Mary Rogers. Born in Derbyshire. First trained and worked as a lettering artist and illustrator. Later studied pottery and set up her studio in 1960, concentrating on hand-modelled methods of working. The forms and decoration of the work evolve both from the particular characteristics of coil and pinch-building in porcelain and stoneware, and from close observation of the forms and patterns of the natural world. This is described in her articles for *Ceramic Review*: No 9 (1971) and No 38 (1976) and in her book on hand-building and designing from natural forms, *Pottery and Porcelain – a Hand-builder's Approach*, which was first published in Britain, the USA and Germany in 1979; updated and republished in 1984. Demonstrated the hand-building techniques for the BBC television series, *The Craft of the Potter*. Her work has been exhibited widely throughout the world since 1960, and is included in many collections such as: The Victoria and Albert Museum; The Metropolitan Museum, New York; The Museum of Modern Art, New York; The Fitzwilliam Museum, Cambridge; The Crafts Council Collection; Boyman's Museum, Rotterdam; The Keramion, Germany; Musee du Cinquantenaire, Brussels; Musee des Arts Decoratifs, Lausanne; Vestlandske Kunstindustriemuseum, Bergen; Perth Art Gallery and Museum, Melbourne City Art Gallery and the National Gallery of Victoria, Australia. She is an Elected Life Member of the International Academy of Ceramics.

Phil Rogers 110

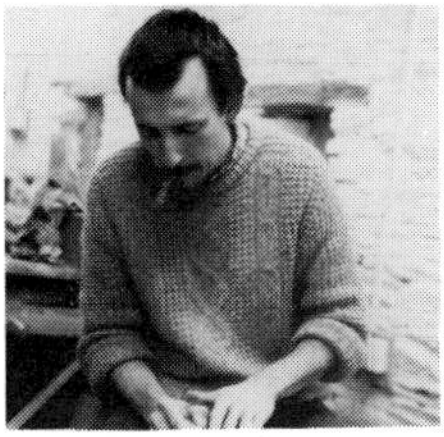

Phil Rogers. Nearly all my pots are thrown and the majority are ash glazed sometimes over a local clay slip. The decoration is either cut, combed, faceted or drawn into the clay mostly while still on the wheel. Sometimes glaze is wiped away while still wet to reveal either the body or a red shino underglaze. Recently I have been using coloured slips under an ash felspar glaze. The body is based on S.M.D. Ball clay and doughmixed. At present the pots are fired in a relatively small, propane fired kiln although I have almost completed a new 60 cu.ft. oil fired kiln. A salt kiln is also planned for completion during the winter of 1985. During the summer of 1985 we held a series of successful weekly courses and these are again planned for 1986, details of which can be obtained by writing to me at the pottery from February onwards. Pots have been purchased for the following public collections: Newport Museum and Art Gallery; National Museum of Wales; University of Wales Collection; Powys and Dyfed County Councils and West Midlands County Council.

David Scott   III

D.S.

David Scott was born in Yorkshire, trained at Stoke-on-Trent and Royal College of Art (1973-76), established workshop in North London in 1977, moved to East London in 1980. Became full time lecturer at Loughborough college of Art in 1983 and moved to present workshop in Leicestershire. Makes individual hand-built pieces, occasionally incorporating throwing techniques. At the moment the work consists of interpretations of traditional forms such as vases. tea-pots and dishes with an emphasis on contrasts of 3-dimensional shape and 2-dimensional surface quality.

Ray Silverman 112

Ray Silverman trained at Camberwell School of Art and Crafts and Goldsmiths' College, London. Exhibited widely in United Kingdom and abroad. Lecturer at West Ham College and Goldsmith's College. Fellow of the Society of Designer Craftsmen. Over the past few years has devoted his time to producing individual thrown forms in stoneware and porcelain.

Michael (and Elizabeth) Skipwith work on their own. Both trained at Leeds College of Art during the 1950s when Ronald Cooper was tutor. They started up Lotus Pottery in 1957 and expanded rapidly to a peak at one time of employing 17, producing coloured glaze earthenware fired by electricity, until 1979. During this period Michael put the Lotus Dischead on the market together with other 'wheel' related accessories, and to this day continues to supply potters throughout the world with this useful accessory. He also currently supplies some of the many hundreds of potters in the South West with raw materials from the Staffordshire Company – Potclays. In 1979 they closed the pottery completely and had a major alteration of the layout and use of the premises in their big old Stoke Gabriel farm. Recommencing in 1981 with a limited production of gas fired individual stoneware and porcelain, Michael then built what has proved to be a very efficient woodfired kiln of about 22 cu.ft. and due to the enthusiasm of Elizabeth for gardening began to specialise in garden and house plant pots. At the time of writing he continues to specialise in unglazed wood fired stoneware garden pots, as well as a limited production of glazed tableware with some porcelain. Both have been and still are active members of the Devon Guild of Craftsmen and apart from the occasional C.P.A. exhibition have only exhibited their pots with this Guild.

Mildred Slatter

Mildred Slatter. Stoneware and porcelain. Won a scholarship to Reading University School of Art in 1926 with a Distinction Diploma. Subsequently took a post graduate course at the Central School of Art and Craft, London, studying weaving with jewellery subsidiary. From there, took over a weaving studio at Heal's of Tottenham Court Road, designing and weaving rugs and tapestries. Then came the six years of the war and subsequent austerity made it difficult to set up a weaving studio again. I, therefore, began to learn to make pots. Joined C.P.A, shortly after its inception and found the early meetings in the old Lowndes Court shop extremely helpful. Part-time teacher at the School of Art in High Wycombe for some years and more recently at the Langley College of Further Education. Work has been exhibited in London, Bath, Southampton, Lincoln, Oxford, High Wycombe, Chalfont St. Giles, Datchet and various small galleries. Workshop is a converted stable and coach-house with one gas kiln and one electric kiln. The stoneware body is made up in the workshop and the porcelain is David Leach's. For the last two years I have been building a collection of ceramic models of steam engines of all kinds. The next and last category will be steamboats, launches and tugs. Fellow and council member of the Society of Designer-Craftsmen for whom I have organised exhibitions.

Frank Smith

Frank Smith. Born 1927 Sydney, Australia. Worked in partnership with my father on nursery in NW Kent growing plants and flowers. Moved to South Darenth to a small farm in 1950. Began making pots in 1962, using wood to once fire pots. Kiln resembled blackened heap of bricks owing to constant alterations. Worked as assistant to Colin Pearson for a year 18 years ago. Accepted as full member of CPA 1971. Moved to present address in 1976. Built catenary arch trolley hearth kiln oil fired. Making stoneware, porcelain and garden pots.

Peter Smith. Formerly a research chemist specialising in high temperature chemistry. Started Bojewyan Pottery in 1974. Currently making two types of work. (1) Earthenware vessels, often slip decorated, and fired in a large coal burning kiln with an open setting allowing flame to impinge on the surfaces. A number of novel making techniques are used on these vessels sometimes several different ones on the same piece. One such technique has the effect of replacing the horizontal wheelhead with a vertical equivalent allowing the freedom of the horizontal movement of the hands across the wheelhead to be transferred to the vertical plane. This enables, for example, strong gestural throwing marks to be preserved. (2) Objects made of unfired clay where the stability has been produced by mixing clay with cement instead of firing in the kiln. Therefore the visual and tactile properties of clay in the raw state are maintained. It is possible by this method to produce mixed media objects involving, say, metal or to work very simply and directly, maintaining the force of the idea, which may otherwise be reduced if the clay were fired. Work in many public and private collections including the Victoria and Albert Museum, London.

John Solly established the present pottery in 1953, in buildings which had been originally built as a basket works in about 1820. Started making pots at Maidstone School of Art, in 1945, under the guidance of Percy Brown and later Gwylym Thomas. Afterwards at Central School with Dora Billington. Spent very short working periods with Wally Cole, at Rye Pottery, and Ray Finch at Winchcombe. Makes domestic repetition and individual pots in high fired earthenware and slipware. Uses red and buff clays with additional local sand. Since 1960 he has been running an annual summer school. He was one of the founder members of the CPA and founder chairman of the flourishing Kent Potters Association. Fellow of the Society of Designer Craftsmen. Having lived and worked in Maidstone all his working life to date, is hoping to move into the country before long, to continue potting and running the summer schools.

Gary Standige 118

Gary Standige studied ceramics at Stoke-on-Trent College of Art 1964-1967 and the Royal College of Art from 1967-1970. Awarded 'The Sanderson' scholarship by the RCA in 1970 to study and travel in America. Taught full-time from 1974-1981 on the vocational ceramics course at Medway College of Design, Kent. Presently Senior Lecturer in ceramics at West Surrey College of Art and Design. Individual pieces in stoneware and porcelain. Major exhibitions: Kapelhuis Gallery Amersfoort Group Show, Kunst and Gewerbe Museum Hamburg Group Show, CPA London three person show, Forum Form Gemenswerth Sigel Group Show, Modern English Porcelain Franz Zimmerman Gallery Zug Switzerland 1980; Modern English Porcelain Basle Switzerland, Henry Rothschild Biennial Exhibition Kettles Yard Cambridge, Large Pot Exhibition, British Crafts Centre, CPA, Basle Switzerland 1981; Amalgam Gallery 1982; Southampton Museum, CPA Victoria and Albert Museum 1983. Work in many private and public collections including acquisitions by the Victoria and Albert Museum, London.

Peter Starkey. Saltglazed stoneware domestic and individual pieces. Lecturer in Ceramics at Cardiff College of Art.

Peter Stoodley

Peter Stoodley makes unglazed, inlaid slip decorated, stoneware planters fired in an electric kiln. Studied originally painting at the Bournemouth and at Goldsmith's Schools of Art, London. Took Art Teachers Diploma at the London Institute of Education in 1947 and during this year chose pottery as a craft subject together with bookbinding. This was done at the Camberwell School of Art. Started Pottery Centre at High Barnet in 1948 for two years. Worked at Poole Pottery in making shop for one year and began teaching part time at Bournemouth College of Art in 1951. Remained there in various capacities until retirement in 1980, full time from 1961. Set up first workshop at Ferndown, Dorset in 1952. Built coke and drip feed oil kilns and throwing wheel and dug clay off the moor. Some work sent to New Zealand. At this time received first commission for plant pots and these have remained primary concern ever since. Moved to present workshop in Bournemouth in 1963. During years 1957-63 was associated with Saviac Workshops in building and developing the original Saviac geared, wooden framed kick wheel and numerous gas and electric kilns. Joined CPA in 1958. Recent exhibitions: Suffolk Craft Society "Pots & Potters" Aldeburgh, 1982 and 1984; Studio Ceramics Today, Victoria and Albert Museum, 1983; Katharine House Gallery, Marlborough, 1984; Newbury Spring Festival, 1985.

Warren and Debora Storch 121

Warren and Debora Storch Through all the changing circumstances of our studio's life, the basic idea of Lawers Farm Pottery has remained unchanged. Our concerns have always been with form and function, and the range of thrown pots which we make is simple and direct and responds well to the needs of either the kitchen or the restaurant. Wood-fired kiln – three acre walled garden.

Harry Horlock Stringer. One of the 1950s wave of 'Painter turned Potter' who had to teach themselves, he found a new way of understanding the formulation and making of glazes without resort to the use of molecular formulae. Always very interested in teaching, he built a school, literally with his bare hands. This was opened in 1965 and has catered for a large international summer school ever since. An interest in Raku in the late fifties led to the first book on this subject to be written in the West in 1967 also designing and making an electric Raku kiln safe enough to use in the classroom in 1965. Being confined to the use of electricity only, much research has gone into the development of quality in oxidising atmospheres, this led to the discovery of the first 'Reactive Slip' in 1975. Served for nine years on the Council of the Craftsman Potters Association during its formative years and was Editor of their Journal for a number of years. He continues to contribute to potters' journals. In the fifties he had a workshop in the old Fulham Pottery making once-fired earthenware for domestic use later transferring to Taggs Yard where twice fired earthenware was made. At present stoneware and a small amount of porcelain, mostly for domestic use is produced. Work has been exhibited in a number of different countries where it is in museums and private collections. He was head of an art department in a Teacher Training College for many years and lectures at home and abroad by invitation.

Helen Swain. I make functional ware and individual forms in all clays, now preferring earthenware and handbuilding. Studied Willesden School of Art (1945-1951) painting, pottery and terracotta. Always feel grateful for the fine teaching I had there, in drawing, and the training of eye and hand. After N.D.D. I spent three months in Cornwall with Harry and May Davis, a wonderful experience, leaving to do A.T.C. at Hornsey College of Art. Then three very happy years, working with Agnete Hoy, for Royal Doulton (Lambeth), where I learned so much from Nita. Hand carving and brush painting; with saltglaze and Bristol ware. Later I taught at Hornsey College of Art for seven years until the birth of my first child. Since 1963 I have been teaching part time at Goldsmiths' College, London. As a founder member of CPA I had a solus exhibition in 1961 and have contributed to 13 groups since then, mainly in London. Since 1977 I have become very interested in the ideas of Carl Jung, and consequently in Art Therapy (for greater self-awareness), using paint and clay, sometimes with groups. Now I try to put into sculptures, ceramics, forms, visual imagery and intuitions, and I need to know rather clearly what is to be expressed by the forms, and a meaningful pattern/decoration evolves. Very early unglazed pots mean most to me now. British ceramic sculpture too, very exciting. Form has always been my prime motivation with decoration quietly related to it.

Geoffrey Swindell

Geoffrey Swindell was born in Stoke-on-Trent 1945, studied at Stoke-on-Trent College of Art (1960-67), Royal College of Art (1967-70). Now lectures at South Glamorgan Institute of Higher Education, Cardiff. "I work with porcelain making very precise forms on the potters wheel. I use a variety of glazes paying great attention to the surface colour and texture. Each piece is very small and one of a kind. I produce only a limited number of pots each year. I have contributed to many exhibitions in many countries." Examples of work in the following public collections: Reading, Bradford, Portsmouth, Leicester, Swindon, Birmingham, Royal Scottish Museum; Castle Museum, Norwich; Abbot Hall Museum, Kendal; Crafts Council; West Riding of Yorkshire Educational Authority; Welsh Arts Council; University College of Wales, Aberystwyth; Art and History Museum, Brussels; Princessenhof Museum, Leeuwarden, Holland; Victoria and Albert Museum, London; Museum of Decorative Arts, Lausanne, Switzerland; Bellerive Museum, Switzerland; Museum of Applied Arts, Sydney, Australia; National Gallery of Victoria, Australia; Museum of Hannover, W. Germany; Landes Museum, Stuttgart, W. Germany; Perth Museum, Australia; National Museum of Wales; Newport Museum and Art Gallery; Ulster Museum.

Janice Tchalenko

Janice Tchalenko. Born Rugby Warwickshire, 1942. Harrow College of Art Workshop Pottery Course 1969-71. Set up own workshop with help of Crafts Council Grant. John Ruskin Bursary award, funded by the Guild of St. George, 1980. Part-time teaching at Camberwell School of Art and Crafts and Royal College of Art. Recent exhibitions: Westminster Gallery, Boston USA; British Ceramics for Czechoslovakia, Prague; Artist Potters Now – Oxfordshire County Museum touring exhibition in collaboration with Sothebys Ltd.; Maya Behn Gallery – Zurich 1985; New Domestic Ware – Crafts Council, London; Dienstßeeldende Kunst, Holland; Yew Tree Gallery, Derbyshire; Institute of Contemporary Art, "Fast Forward"; BlumHelman Gallery, New York, 1985. Public Collections: Victoria and Albert Museum, London; Crafts Council, London; Southampton City Museum and Art Gallery; George Wenger Collection, Stoke-on-Trent; Cleveland County Museum Service; Ulster Museum; Shipley Museum; Paisley Museum.

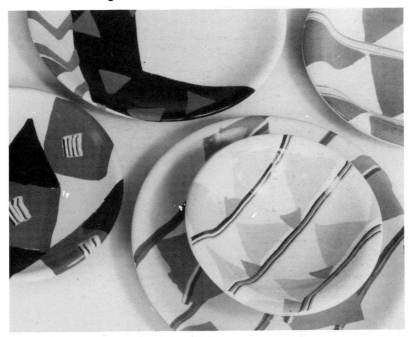

Sabina Teuteberg has a fine-art background and trained in ceramics at Croydon College of Art. Decorates mostly clay slabs with coloured clay inlays and slips. At present the colourful abstract patterned slabs are turned into a range of functional ceramics by the method of jigger and jolley. All work is high fired earthenware. Special commissions undertaken and colour co-ordinated ranges made to order.

Owen Thorpe

Owen Thorpe studied at Willesden Art School (1951-56), Harrow School of Art (1959-61) and Bournemouth College of Art (1961-62). Set up workshop in Ealing, London 1970. Moved to Priestweston, Shropshire 1975, Churchstoke, Powys 1981. Works alone. Produces a range of domestic stoneware pottery using coloured and locally occurring slips and wax-resist decoration. All work is wheel-thrown and is fired with electric oxidising firing. Also produces range of garden pottery decorated with coloured slip brushwork as well as highly decorated individual pieces using a technique like majolica but at stoneware temperatures. Tin glazes are employed, some tinted cream or light blue, with elaborate brushed patterns applied to the unfired glaze. Group exhibitions: CPA, Threehouseholds Gallery (1974); Lantern Gallery Manchester (1979); Oriel 31 Welshpool Powys (1984); Stratford Art Gallery, Wolverhampton Art Gallery, Sept. 1985.

Vera Tollow   128

Tollow

Vera Tollow. After studying at Croydon College of Art, taking N.D.D. in textile design and pottery, I set up my pottery studio in a former stable block in Wallington. Working alone, I produce a range of domestic stoneware as well as larger individual pieces. Most pots are made on the wheel, fired in a gas kiln with reducing atmosphere to bring out the quality of ash glazes. Decoration is usually by brush, slip or sgraffito or combinations. A varied selection of work is normally available for wholesale customers to make 'off the shelf' selection thus relieving me of the pressure of 'making to order'.

Marianne de Trey. Born in London of Swiss parents. Trained at the Royal College of Art. Widow of the potter and painter T.S. Haile. Produced slipware for a year in a Suffolk brickyard and then moved to Dartington in 1947, where she has worked ever since. For many years she ran a workshop with three assistants, making standard tableware, first in earthenware and then in oxidised stoneware. She later developed her own more personal work in porcelain and stoneware using a small oil kiln and one fired with wood, and produced a series of pots for flower arranging. She has recently phased out the domestic range of stoneware and works alone, concentrating on 'one offs' mostly in porcelain. The porcelain is hand thrown and of fairly traditional form, but is decorated with many different techniques sometimes in very strong colours and shows her deep love of pattern, derived mostly from natural objects but also from the textiles which were her first love. She was an early member of the Craftsmen Potters Association and is on the Design Index. Exhibitions in London, Amsterdam, Cambridge, Boston, Geisenheim, Bristol, Guildford, Folkestone, Exeter, Plymouth and other towns in the South West. Retrospective shows in Cider Press Centre in 1983 and in Bristol 1984, J.K. Hill in 1984 and Long Street Gallery in 1985.

Angela Verdon. All the one off pieces are very finely cast with incised and pierced surfaces which utilise and enhance the translucency of the medium. The piercings exploit to the full the fine delicate nature of bone china as well as its great strength. The bone china slip is poured into plaster moulds and tipped 10 to 30 seconds later (depending on size of the piece). Once the slip has dried out and shrank from the side of the mould the piece is removed and fired to a temperature of 1100°C — at this stage the material is soft enough to withstand the pressure of the process. After the surface decoration is applied the work is fired to 1220°C and finally hand burnished to achieve a semi-matt sheen. Recently I have incorporated colour into my work by applying body stains to porcelain clays. The laminated pieces are produced by casting a layer of white slip tipping and allowing to dry — casting a layer of body stained slip, tipping etc. — building up the layers of varying widths. The completed piece is then removed from the mould the surface ground, shaped and cut — finally fired to 1220°C and hand burnished.

Aw W.

Alan Wallwork. First workshop in 1957 in Forest Hill, South London, after some brief but stimulating experience, thanks to Kenneth Clark and Gordon Baldwin, of ceramics at Goldsmiths' College, London. In 1960 workshop moved to Greenwich and then, in 1964, to Marnhull, Dorset. Hand decorated tile production had come to be a steady, easily controlled, mainstay enabling a number of assistants to be regularly employed who were also available to help with the more erratic parallel production of a wide range of handbuilt, reduction fired stoneware, mostly sculptural pieces influenced by natural forms. By 1984 it seemed time to dispose of the Marnhull workshops and find a quieter existence high on a wooded hill overlooking the sea and the Dorset coastline from Lyme Regis to Portland Bill. Tile production is in abeyance and sculptural stoneware will probably now be the main output, perhaps with occasional batches of garden pots made from the local clay. The textural, tactile qualities of ceramic surfaces continue to be the main fascination.

Sarah Walton

Sarah Walton was born in 1945 and grew up in London and Selmeston, Sussex. She originally studied painting, then changed to nursing, but reverted to working in the arts, this time in Studio Pottery. After studying on the Harrow Pottery Course and working for David Leach and then Zelda Mowat, she set up her own workshop at Selmeston, seven miles from Lewes, in 1975. She has worked there since that time. All her pots are saltglazed. In this technique, the effects of chance play a considerable part in determining the final glaze, and the role of the potter is rather to exploit these natural occurrences than to dictate preconceived effects. In England today a small fraction of potters employ this technique. She uses both throwing and hand-building techniques. She works within a style of simple and austere forms. Recent solo exhibitions: The Southover Gallery, Lewes, Sussex 1976-1984; Craftsmen Potters Shop, London W.1 (with potters Andrew and Joanna Young) 1981; Findlay College, Ohio, USA 1982; The Terrace Gallery, Worthing, Sussex 1983. Work in Public Collections: Crafts Council, London; Victoria & Albert Museum, London; Contemporary Arts Society, London; South East Arts Collection; Nottingham Museum.

John Ward   133

John Ward. Born in London in 1938. Started potting 1965 when, while working as a BBC cameraman, I attended part-time at a Studio Pottery course at East Ham Technical College in East London. In 1966 accepted at Camberwell School of Art and Crafts for a four year Dip.A.D. course. I set up my first workroom in 1970 and taught part-time at an Adult Education Institute until 1979 when I moved to Wales to pot full-time. All of my work is handbuilt by pinching out a base then adding strips of clay. The final form is sometimes altered by making cuts and rejoining to produce ridges or grooves. I am interested in hollow forms, especially bowls, function being secondary to form. I fire in an electric kiln, biscuit firing to 1000°C, glaze 1250°C. Glazes are applied by a combination of pouring and spraying, sometimes with oxides underneath rubbed into texture or applied in banded designs. At present I use five matt stoneware glazes in various combinations; a white, a black, a blue/green, a brown/black/blue and a yellow. Since 1971 I have taken part in many group exhibitions in the U.K., Germany and the U.S.A. Solo exhibitions: 1982 Peter Dingley Gallery, Stratford-upon-Avon; 1985 Craftsmen Potters Shop.

Sasha Wardell   134

SKW '85

Sasha Wardell. The pieces are slipcast bone china, all of which are individually decorated. The models are turned on a plaster lathe then carved by hand to introduce twists and facets. After moulding they are cast thinly to enhance translucency then fired to 1260°C. Some are decorated before the high firing by a means of stained slip sections laid into the mould prior to casting. The other pieces are decorated by means of an airbrush through a series of retreating masks and fired a second time. They are all polished by hand to achieve an egg-shell finish. Born Negombo, Sri Lanka 1956, studied at Cambridgeshire College of Arts and Technology, Cambridge, Bath Academy of Art, Corsham, Wiltshire (1976-79), M.A. in Design (Ceramics) at North Staffordshire Polytechnic, Stoke-on-Trent (1979-1980). Major exhibitions at British Crafts Centre; Katharine House Gallery; Beaux Arts Gallery, Bath; Graham Gallery, New York; Yew Tree Gallery, Ashbourne and New Ashgate Gallery, Farnham.

Robin Welch 135

ROBIN
WELCH

Robin Welch. The pottery is a mile out of Stradbroke on the B1118. Wilby Road, two hours from London. A range of domestic stoneware is produced using the jigger and jolley technique. Individual pots and sculpture are also made. A basic feldspar glaze with wood ash gives rich earthy colours fired in a 100 cu.ft. trolly hearth kiln to 1300°C in a reduced atmosphere. Domestic ware has been accepted by the Council of Industrial Design and exhibited in the Design Centre regularly. Trained at Nuneaton and Penzance School of Art, worked part-time at the Leach Pottery, St. Ives, and at Central School of Art and Design, London. Spent three years working in Australia. Exhibited in many countries and pots in many museums and galleries.

Tony Weston. Born 1941. One year's evening class at Harrow (Mick Casson). Full-time potter for twenty years. Confirmed raw-glazer. At present using fast-fire electric kiln because it suits the rapid turn-round necessitated by my 'al fresco' routine. All work in the Summer is thrown, on a portable kickwheel of my own design, under God's trees in All Saints' garden, opposite Trinity in Cambridge. (This market is run by Cambridge City Council for local Craft-people, Fridays and Saturdays in the Summer). The search for a prepared clay which could be cut straight from the bag, perversely, has led to the use of two stoneware and one earthenware clay, which look relatively wholesome at 1230/1240°C, the snag being that I have to slab and wedge them *in situ*. As compensation I have the fun of providing percussion for the Market's resident Melodeon-player.

John Wheeldon. Born Matlock, Derbyshire 1950. Studied Chesterfield College of Art and Design, The Polytechnic, Wolverhampton (1974). My work is produced almost entirely in either porcelain or a black stoneware. All is thrown and subsequently turned, and my aim during this part of the process is to attempt to give the forms life and cadence while at the same time preparing and making decisions about the areas of the pot which will later be decorated. I enjoy drawing out of a clay body the various textures that are inherent in it. To this end I use various ribs to form the pots and modify the surfaces during throwing. I have the same approach to turning – using the tools to modify the surface. Following turning the pots are bisque fired to 1000°C and subsequently glazed using a few simple matt white or clear glazes, with occasional coloured glazes – mainly matts. Glaze firing is carried out in a Propane gas kiln to 1275°C reduction. The final surface is important as it vitally affects the appearance and feel of the finished lustre, different effects being achieved on matt, textured or shiny surfaces. The decoration is applied using resist, soft-rubber stamps and brush to apply various coloured and metallic lustres. Firing to cone 018 in a small top-loading electric kiln completes the process. In decorating I aim to create a sense of richness both in colour and visual texture. Recent exhibitions: Yewtree Gallery Derbyshire, Rufford Crafts Centre, Stoke-on-Trent City Museum and Art Gallery, 1982; Marie Jordan Gallery Wakefield, David Canter Memorial Exhibition C.P.A. 1984; New Members Exhibition C.P.A., Long Street Gallery Tetbury Gloucestershire 1985.

Mary White 138

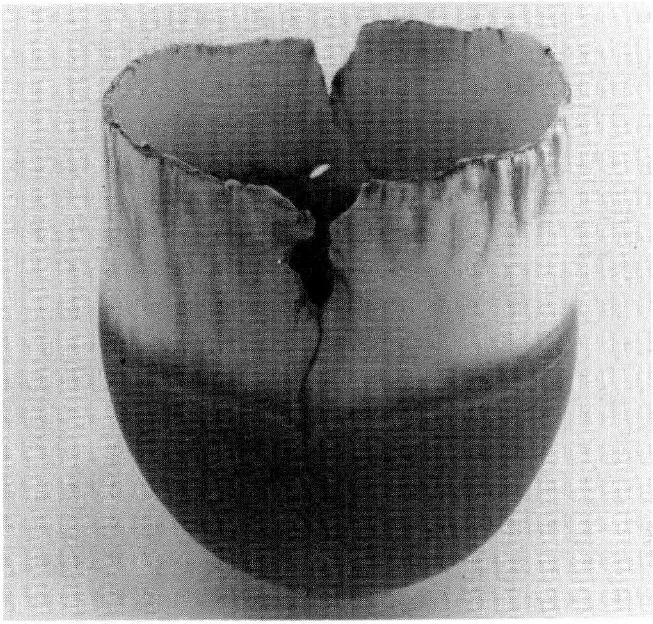

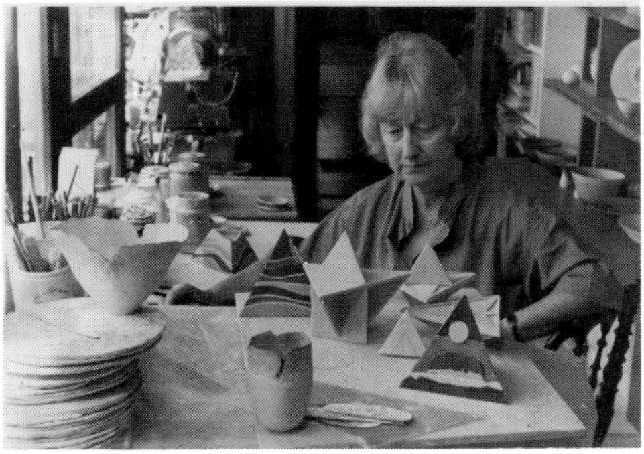

Mary White. Art training 1943-50 (Art Teachers Diploma, Goldsmiths' College, London 1950). Set up Ceramic Workshop 1971, Wales. First one-person show, London 1973 (Commonwealth Gallery). Moved to Wiltshire 1975. Moved to Germany 1980. Exhibited widely in Europe and U.S.A. etc. Seminars in Britain and Germany. Work in international Museums and Collections. Awarded Staatspreis Rheinland-Pfalz 1982 (Federal prize for outstanding Craftwork). After teaching for 10 years in an International College (Atlantic College), Charles and I left to produce our own work full-time. Missing the contacts with other countries and their cultures we moved into the 'Centre of Europe'. Since exhibiting in many one-person and large group exhibitions all over Germany, our 'neighbour' countries and U.S.A. I am finding that my work is becoming more experimental and sculptural. I am constantly torn between organic and geometric forms; spontaneous and contemplated ideas; soft and hard. I am slowly learning to combine these. The subtlely undulating landscape of our vineyard surroundings and my nostalgia for the sea are becoming a new source of inspiration. Harder forms stem from an interest in Egyptian Art, especially pyramids, the world as a sphere, and the cosmos. At the moment I am experimenting with body colours and coloured slips. Together with sculptural ceramics I am still developing new treatments for wide-flanged bowls, which I have always made, and classical forms.

Geoffrey Whiting. Although interested in pottery as a boy, making crude pots and kilns in the garden at home, his only formal training was in architecture. Eight and a half years army service, and contact with Indian village potters, 'killed' architecture and, with little more than an intuitive feeling for clay and fire, he started Avoncroft Pottery in Worcestershire, making domestic slipware, then stoneware, with some individual pieces. After moving to larger premises in 1955, and the building of a second wood-fired kiln, in 1972 circumstances took him to Canterbury and eventual contact with the King's School, where he now combines a reduced production of stoneware and porcelain with teaching. He has taught part-time and lectured widely and has had student apprentices from many parts of the world. His work is represented in twenty-three public collections here and overseas, and he sells through the CPA shop and a small group of retailers. Despite the dubious and wayward trend in much modern ceramics, at prices to match, he remains convinced that the 'traditional pot' must always be the basis for work of lasting value.

Caroline Whyman

Caroline Whyman first went to art school with the intention of becoming a painter, but as soon as I was introduced to clay I knew I'd become a potter. I studied at Camberwell School of Art (1969-72) when there was a strong bias towards studio ceramics. Then started a workshop with two other students at what was to become "Camden Lock". To my surprise I have taught part-time since in Adult Education, which I find rewarding and a counterpoint to working quietly away in my workshop. At Camden I threw domestic ware, large coiled planters, and slabbed. Gradually I have started working more with porcelain — it seemed to have the possibilities I wanted: stronger, clearer colours at high temperatures and the precision that was possible through turning and combining shapes at the leather-hard stage. In 1981 moved to the workshop in Islington where I have concentrated on making one-off pieces — vases, bowls and boxes (which I throw in one piece and separate by turning). I still fire my work in a 12 cubic foot electric kiln which I've had since 1973. I swear every time I pack it that a smaller one would be cheaper and quicker to fire, but I'm accustomed to its idiosyncrasies. I exhibit regularly every year and sell work through the Craftsmen Potters Association and my workshop.

David Winkley |4|

David Winkley originally trained as a painter at the School of Fine Art, Reading University and at Pembroke College, Cambridge. He began making pots at Dartington in 1963 and opened his first pottery in Bristol the following year. Since 1966 he has been in his present workshop. With the help of his assistant, Timothy Jay, he now produces one of the widest ranges of functional stoneware of any small pottery in Britain plus individual pieces in both stoneware and porcelain. He is particularly interested in decoration using brushwork, wax-resist and glaze on glaze techniques. A chance encounter with Harry Davis in 1971 convinced him that selective mechanisation can play a significant part in craftwork production, releasing time and energy for more creative and profitable work. In consequehce all the mundane preparation of clay bodies and glazes at Vellow is now done by machine, only the actual making of pots is by hand. Glaze and biscuit firings take place simultaneously in a two-chambered oil fired kiln of some 230 cu.ft. capacity built in 1985. It combines traditional kiln building materials with modern ceramic fibres.

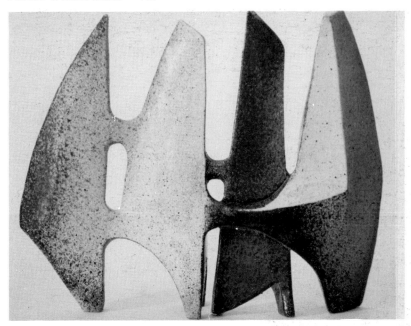

Mollie Winterburn. My beginnings in ceramics were haphazard but determined. Many years a P.E. teacher, I took out children, dug clay, made pots, fired in the playing fields, visited every available potter from a plant-pot maker to Leach and became instead a pottery teacher. Later in charge of 3D work in a London comprehensive; an examiner; author of two books on handbuilt pottery, one published in London and one in New York; then a senior lecturer in ceramics in a London College. I have been a full time member of CPA since 1958. An accident in 1972 curtailed clay work. In 1979 began rebuilding hill farm into home and studios. Back to clay, after period of painting and printmaking; additional kiln on way. While thoroughly enjoyed all teaching, resented being unable to leave it before retirement age, because of lack of time for my own work. But advantages − no necessity to repeat, or accept unwanted commissions. Throughout managed to exhibit and have work in public and private collections here and abroad. Work always 'one-off', mostly handbuilt and mostly stoneware. Primary interest is in form. Bottles a recurring interest because of full body and tiny neck; and always human. Now mostly work on themes − may stem from a totally non-representational form, though recently 'Heads', 'Journeys' and 'Walks'. Age may slow work but ideas are non-stop.

Mary Wondrausch. I work in red earthenware, using Fremington best clay for the hollow wares and Potclays 1135 for the large plates and dishes. My pouring slip is Bideford pipe clay which comes to us as quarried and I use TWVD white ball clay from Watts, Blake & Bearne for the trailing slips. I use a sesquisilicate from Potterycrafts for my glaze and fire to 1050°C in a Cromartie electric kiln. I work in approximately two different ways: sgraffito and slip trailing. The first is scratching through the leather hard clay to the body and enhancing the drawing with brushed copper under a honey glaze. These jugs and mugs usually have jolly verses taken from the 18th Century potters' work or from Ogden Nash or Yeats. I also use the same technique for similar pots but in this case I use cobalt to enhance the drawing under a clear glaze. Still using the sgraffito technique but working in a freer and more 'painterly' way, I use 4 different oxides to colour the picture that I have made on a cheese platter. The second way is slip trailing commemorative plates to celebrate births, marriages, anniversaries, presentations, and so on. This is my bread-and-butter line which I particularly enjoy as it enables me to have personal contact with my customer. My inspiration originally came from 17th Century Staffordshire work but latterly Hungarian, German and Swiss decorations and pots have influenced me. I moved my pottery from Godalming to my own 17th Century house in Compton, converting the stable, in October 1984. I find this beautiful rural environment is having quite a profound effect on my work. For example, I work longer hours, and the flowers and butterflies and chickens that come into the workshop also come on to the plates.

Nigel Wood

Nigel Wood. A potter since 1965. Trained at the traditional terracotta workshops of S & E Collier Ltd., Reading, and A. Harris & Sons, Wrecclesham, Farnham, Surrey, where learned big-ware making. Art training at Berkshire College of Art and West Surrey College of Art, Farnham. (Farnham 1969-1972). Established Meon Pottery, West Meon, Hampshire in partnership in 1973. Worked there full and part-time, making stoneware, porcelain and terracotta until 1984. Still partner in Meon Pottery, but workshop is presently run by terracotta potter Michael Pinner. Very interested in Far Eastern Ceramics. Book *Oriental Glazes* (Pitman Publishing) 1978. Currently re-writing and updating it for A & C Black. Currently Research Fellow in Ceramic History, West Surrey College of Art and Design, Lecturer in Ceramic Theory, W.S.C.A.D. and Visiting Lecturer, Faculty of Art, Southampton Institute. Since 1985 registered for M.Phil/Ph.D in collaboration with Oxford University. Has worked in collaboration with Oxford University's Archaeology Research Laboratory since 1982, and published a number of research papers on Far Eastern ceramics (particularly porcelain) in Japan, China, U.S.A. and U.K. Delivered paper on Chinese porcelain technology to the Second International Conference on Ancient Chinese Pottery and Porcelain, held in Beijing, China in 1985. Mark: − no mark at present. (Meon mark now used by Michael Pinner).

Rosemary Wren and Peter Crotty 145, 31

Rosemary Wren and Peter Crotty. Lustleigh, a beautiful village in a valley on the eastern fringes of Dartmoor, is now the home of The Oxshott Pottery — believed to be Britain's oldest existing studio workshop. It was originally established in 1920 by Rosemary's parents, Denise and Henry Wren, at Oxshott in Surrey, having begun in 1912 when Denise bought a potter's wheel and set up as part of the Knox Guild of Design and Craft at Kingston-upon-Thames. Pots and records from these times are now in the Museum there and at the Crafts Study Centre, Holburne Museum, Bath. Rosemary joined the pottery in 1950. Peter became Rosemary's partner in 1970; the work on each piece is now divided between them. After leaving the Hall School, Weybridge, Rosemary worked with animals for four years. She then studied at Guildford School of Art and the Royal College of Art — owing most to Helen Pincombe as pottery teacher, and to Willi Soukop for sculpture. She became a competent and sensitive thrower, but found lasting scope to put together her abilities and her interests in a 'pinched-coil' method of making pot-shaped animal forms which she learnt from Albert Diato and Francine Delpierre in 1953. Such animals have always been made by potters using the techniques ordinarily employed to make hollow vessels. Antecedents are to be found in any ethnographical museum. Rosemary constructs each piece individually, following her own sketches from life, and defining the outline of the pattern with an incised line. Peter then takes over, first biscuit firing, and then realising the tone and colour of the pattern with a palette of both matt and flowing glazes. The skill required for the brushwork, as also a sense of colour, was acquired during two years of gouache painting. On one piece ten different glazes may be needed, all firing together to stoneware temperatures in a Calor gas kiln. Their animals and birds have been widely exhibited and collected. Rosemary was a gold medallist at the Prague International in 1962; other venues for group exhibitions have included the Royal Scottish Academy (1965), the Commonwealth Institute (1973) and the Victoria and Albert Museum (1973, 1975, 1983) and for individual shows the Berkeley Galleries, the Craftsmen Potters Shop, Casson Gallery, London and Dartington Cider Press amongst many others. A Retrospective Exhibition of the Oxshott Pottery was held at the Crafts Study Centre, Bath in 1984. Rosemary and Peter are also members of the Devon Guild of Craftsmen and Rosemary was founding chairman of the Craftsmen Potters' Association. They have written extensively for *Ceramic Review* and given many lectures and seminars. Their work is to be found in selected craft galleries, and may also be bought or ordered direct from the studio. List of 80 creatures, with prices (£14-£350) on application (SAE please). Packing for postal or other delivery is gladly undertaken at cost.

Takeshi Yasuda. Apprenticeship at The Daisei Pottery Mashiko, Japan (1963-66). Established own workshop in Mashiko. Worked in U.K. since 1973. Many group and solo exhibitions including The Victoria and Albert Museum; British Crafts Centre; Craftsmen Potters Shop; Ulster Museum Belfast; Southampton Art Gallery; The National Museum of Applied Art Oslo, Norway; the Crafts Council Gallery; Jissan Institute Oxford University, Kettles Yard Cambridge and Dulwich Picture Gallery.

A. & J. YOUNG POTTERY

Joanna and Andrew Young. Dip.A.D. Ceramics at W.S.C.A.D. Farnham, Surrey (1970-73). Worked in France with Gwyn Hanssen for 6 months. A.T.C. Goldsmith's College, University of London. 1975 set up workshop at Hunworth, North Norfolk with Crafts Council Grant. Built 100 cu.ft. oil fired kiln. Developed a range of practical domestic pots, wheel thrown and raw glazed. Some of the pots are shaped by cutting and squaring off in various ways. The glaze is allowed to settle out before being applied, then reduction fired to 1280°C to produce a finish sometimes mistaken for saltglaze. The clay body is mixed from ball clays, China clay and local sand in a dough mixer and then pugged. 1981, moved to larger workshop in Lower Gresham, Norfolk. Continued making domestic range with the help of two assistants. Recent exhibitions: Gainsborough House Museum, Suffolk, Two Family Show 1982, Victoria & Albert Museum, C.P.A. 25 years Show, British Craft Centre Travelling Exhibition, Australia 1983. Pots bought by V & A Museum, Wenger Collection, Crafts Council travelling exhibition, New Domestic Pottery. British Tableware Exhibition, Printemps, Paris, 1985.

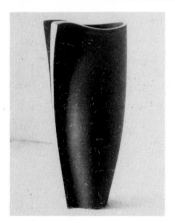

Monica Young. After art school training, practised as painter and book illustrator. Taught herself to coil pots and in 1974 moved to North Yorkshire to establish a workshop and to take up pottery full-time. Makes individually designed stoneware pieces based on traditional and sculptural shapes. The pots are unglazed but, when fired to 1300° in a reduction atmosphere, they acquire a deep 'toasted' colour. Maximum size of pots: 58" × 36". Pieces in public and private collections here and abroad.

Visiting A Potter

This is a full list of names and addresses of members of the CPA, together with details of opening hours. The map gives approximate geographical position. Map numbers correspond to those following the potters' names in the directory.

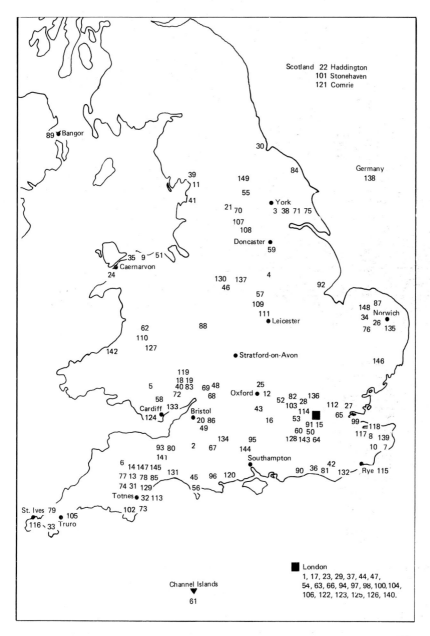

Scotland 22 Haddington
101 Stonehaven
121 Comrie

89 Bangor

30

84

Germany
138

39
11
149
41
55
21 70
107
108

York
3 38 71 75

35 9 51
Caernarvon
24

Doncaster
59

130 137
46
4
92

57
109
111
Leicester

148 87
34 Norwich
26
76 135

62
110
142 127
88

Stratford-on-Avon

146

119
18 19
5 40 83 69 48
72 68
58
Cardiff 133
124
Bristol
20 86
49

25
Oxford 12
52 82 28 136
103 114
43 53 91 15
16 60 50
128 143 64

112 27
65
99 118
117 8 139
10 7

93 80
141
6
14 147 145
77 13 78 85
74 31 129
Totnes 32 113
St. Ives 79
116 33 Truro
105
102 73

2 67
134
95
144
Southampton

131 45 96 120
56

42
90 36 81 132 Rye 115

London
1, 17, 23, 29, 37, 44, 47,
54, 63, 66, 94, 97, 98, 100, 104,
106, 122, 123, 125, 126, 140.

Channel Islands
61

Adrian Abberley   1
Home:
50A Earls Court Square
London SW5

(01) 373 6161

Shop and Pottery:
Cabin Pottery
60A Golborne Road
London W10

Showroom — please phone

John Ablitt   2
The Old Post Office
East Pennard
Shepton Mallet
Somerset

Ditcheat 241 (STD code 074 986)

Visitors welcome by appointment

Mick Arnup   3
Holtby Pottery
Holtby
York YOI 3UA

York 489 377 (STD code 0904)

Showroom open 10.00 — 18.00 daily (Holtby A166
five miles from York)

Chris Aston   4
Chris Aston Pottery
High Street
Elkesley
Nr Retford
Notts. DN22 8AJ

Gamston 391 (STD code 077 783)

Showroom open seven days a week 10am — 6pm
Visitors welcome to workshop

Alan and Ruth Barrett-Danes   5
The Laurels
83 Chapel Road
Abergavenny
Gwent

Abergavenny 4329 (STD code 0873)

Visitors by appointment

Svend Bayer   6
Duckpool Cottage
Sheepwash
Beaworthy
Devon EX21 5PW

Black Torrington 282 (STD code 040 923)

Visitors are welcome but best to telephone first

Michael Bayley   7
Beechcroft Cottage
Green Lane
Temple Ewell
Dover
Kent CT16 3AS

Dover 822624 (STD code 0304)

Visitors are welcome. Please telephone for
directions.

Peter F Beard   8
The Pottery
Bottom Ponds Road
Wormshill
Kent ME9 0TR

Wormshill 554 (STD code 062 784)

Showroom open at any reasonable time but
strictly by appointment

Terry Bell-Hughes   9
Fron Dirion
Conwy Road
Llandudno Junction
Gwynedd, North Wales

Maelgwyn 2575 (STD code 049 261)

Visitors to workshop by appointment only

Tony Benham   10
Everden Farmhouse
Nr Swingfield
Dover CT15 7EH

Hawkinge 3367 (STD code 030 389)

My kiln is not at my workshop, so visitors only
by appointment please.

Maggie Angus Berkowitz   11
21-23 Park Road
Milnthorpe
Cumbria LA7 7AD

Milnthorpe 3970 (STD code 044 82)

Visitors considering commissioning are welcome
at the studio, but should arrange an appointment

Audrey Blackman　12
Wood Croft
Foxcombe Lane
Boars Hill
Oxford OX1 5DH

Oxford 735148 (STD code 0865)

Visitors are welcome by appointment

Clive Bowen　13
Shebbear Pottery
Shebbear
Beaworthy
Devon EX21 5QZ

Shebbear 271 (STD code 040 928)

Wholesale and retail customers are welcome at
the showroom

Sandy Brown　14
Studio Ceramics
38 East Street
South Molton
Devon EX36 3DF

South Molton 2829 (STD code 076 95)

Visitors are welcome by chance or appointment

Ian Byers　15
10 Westbourne Road
Croydon
Surrey CR0 6HP

(01) 654 0225

The studio is not open to the public but work is
sold from there occasionally

Alan Caiger-Smith　16
Aldermaston Pottery
Aldermaston Village
Berkshire RG7 4LW

Woolhampton 71 3359 (STD code 0734)

Opening hours 8am – 5pm, except Sundays

Daphne Carnegy　17
Unit 30 Kingsgate Workshops
110-116 Kingsgate Road
London NW6

(01) 328 2051

Visitors by appointment

Michael Casson　18
Wobage Farm
Upton Bishop
Ross-on-Wye
Herefordshire HR9 7QP

Upton Bishop 233 (STD code 098 985)

Visitors welcome but please telephone first if
possible

Sheila Casson　19
Wobage Farm
Upton Bishop
Ross-on-Wye
Herefordshire HR9 7QP

Upton Bishop 233 (STD code 098 985)

Visitors welcome but please telephone first if
possible

Jenny Clarke　20
25 Etloe Road
Westbury Park
Bristol BS6 7NZ

Bristol 735193 (STD code 0272)

Visitors welcome by appointment

Derek Clarkson　21
1 The Poplars
Bacup
Lancashire OL13 8AD

Bacup 874541 (STD code 0706)

Visitors are welcome to workshop; work usually
on display, at any reasonable time. Advisable to
telephone if making a special journey.

Margery Clinton　22
The Pottery
Newton Port
Haddington
East Lothian

Haddington 3584 (STD code 062 082)

Showroom open Tuesday to Saturday inclusive
10am – 1pm and 2pm – 5.30pm. Closed
Sunday and Monday.

Russell Coates　23
26 Colebrooke Row
London N1 8AS

(01) 226 7764

Visitors welcome but please telephone first

Michael Cole   24
Corlwyni Pottery
Nantmor
Caernarfon
Gwynedd LL55 4YL

Beddgelert 331 (STD code 076 686)

Visitors: Workshop/showroom 9am – 6pm daily.
Summer showroom in village 10am – 4pm daily.

Russell Collins   25
The Pottery
East End Farm House
Hook Norton
Oxon.

Hook Norton 737414 (STD code 0608)

The showroom displays a varied selection of work
and is open 9.30am to 5.30pm Monday to
Saturday

Barbara Colls   26
177 Thunder Lane
Thorpe St Andrew
Norwich NR7 0JF

Norwich 36695 (STD code 0603)

Visitors welcome by appointment

Joanna Constantinidis   27
2 Bells Chase
Great Baddow
Chelmsford
Essex

Chelmsford 71842 (STD code 0245)

Visitors by appointment only

Delan Cookson   28
33A Green Lane
Radnage
High Wycombe
Bucks HP14 4DJ

Radnage 3714 (STD code 024 026)

Visitors welcome by appointment

Emmanuel Cooper   29
Fonthill Pottery
38 Chalcot Road
London NW1 8LP

(01) 722 9090

Visitors welcome by appointment. Monday to
Saturday 10am – 5pm.

Suzi Cree   30
Folly Gill Mill
Leeming Lane
Thornthwaite
Harrogate HG3 2QU

Harrogate 780095 (STD code 0423)

Visitors by appointment only

Peter Crotty   31
The Oxshott Pottery
Mill Cottage
Mill Lane
Lustleigh
Newton Abbot
Devon TQ13 9SS

Lustleigh 231 (STD code 064 77)

Works in partnership with Rosemary Wren q.v.

Dart Pottery   32
(formerly Dartington Pottery)
Shinners Bridge
Dartington
Totnes
Devon TQ9 6JE

Totnes 864163 (STD code 0803)

Visitors welcome by appointment

John Davidson   33
New Mills Pottery
New Mills
Ladock
Truro
Cornwall TR2 4NN

St Austell 882209 (STD code 0726)

Visitors are welcome. Showroom on premises.

Clive Davies   34
The Pottery
Withersdale
Harleston
Norfolk IP20 0JG

Fressingfield 407 (STD code 037 986)

Visitors very welcome but please telephone first
as opening times somewhat erratic.

John Davies   35
Gwynedd Pottery
Y Ffor
Pwllheli
Gwynedd LL53 6RR

Pwllheli 612932 (STD code 0758)

Although I still make pots, I am not in full
production at the present time, partly due to
having to make a living at another occupation
besides pottery in order to help fund eventual
new workshops and also, as a kind of 'sabbatical'
– to relax and re-think about my approach to the
craft. My plan is to be back into full-time pot-
making in mid 1986.

Derek Davis   36
Duff House
Maltravers Street
Arundel
West Sussex

Arundel 882600 STD code 0903)

Visitors preferably by appointment

Sally Dawson   37
2 Albion Square
London E8 4ES

(01) 249 0760

Visitors by appointment

Peter Dick   38
Coxwold Pottery
Coxwold
York YO6 4AA

Coxwold 344 (STD code 034 76)

Visitors are welcome to visit the pottery
showroom and see work in progress. Opening
times: weekdays 10am – 5.30pm. Week-ends and
group visits by appointment

Mike Dodd   39
Wellrash
Boltongate
Carlisle
Cumbria CA5 1DH

Low Ireby 615 (STD code 096 57)

Visitors welcome

Jack Doherty   40
Hook's Cottage
Lea Bailey
Ross-on-Wye
Herefordshire HR9 5TY

Lea 644 (STD code 098 981)

There is a small showroom at the workshop
where visitors are welcome by appointment.

Micky Doherty   41
Mewith Pottery
Bentham
Nr Lancaster

Bentham 61461 (STD code 0468)

Visitors to the showroom welcome, though best
to telephone beforehand.

John Dunn   42
Beach Ceramics
168 The Arches
Kings Road
Brighton
Sussex

Brighton 725013/602299 (STD code 0273)

Visitors welcome by appointment

Geoffrey Eastop   43
The Pottery
Ecchinswell
Nr Newbury
Berkshire RG15 8TT

Kingsclere 298220 (STD code 0635)

Workshop/Showroom open most days by
appointment

David Edmonds   44
45 Devonshire Drive
Greenwich
London SE10

(01) 692 8964

Studio open for viewing most days. A telephone
call first would be appreciated.

David Eeles   45
The Shepherd's Well Pottery
Mosterton
Beaminster
Dorset DT8 3HN

Broadwindsor 68257 (STD code 0308)

New work to be found mainly at retail outlets:
The Pot Shop 56 Broad Street Lyme Regis Dorset,
The Pot Shop A303 Watergore near South
Petherton Somerset and at the Pottery
Showroom, Shepherd's Well Pottery Mosterton
Beaminster Dorset. Opening hours 9am to 5pm
all days. Visitors wishing to see workshop please
make an appointment. Regret no available places
for students in the foreseeable future.

Derek Emms   46
Mossfield Cottage
Hayes Bank
Stone
Staffs. ST15 8SZ

Stone 812048 (STD code 0785)

Visitors to the studio by appointment

Dorothy Feibleman   47
10 Arlingford Road
London SW2

(01) 674 8979

Visitors welcome by appointment

Ray Finch   48
Winchcombe Pottery
Winchcombe
Nr Cheltenham
Glos. GL54 5NU

Winchcombe 602462 (STD code 0242)

Visitors welcome at retail shop and (usually)
workshop. Monday – Friday 9am – 5pm;
Saturday 9am – 1pm. Closed Saturday afternoon
and all day Sunday.

Robert Fournier   49
Fournier Pottery
(Robert and Sheila Fournier)
The Tanyard
Lacock
Chippenham
Wiltshire

Lacock 266 (STD code 024 973)

Visitors welcome at showroom
Telephone call advisable

Sylvia des Fours   50
The Pottery
Heather Hill
Givons Grove
Leatherhead
Surrey KT22 8LB

Leatherhead 372473 (STD code 0372)

Visitors welcome by appointment

David Frith   51
Brookhouse Pottery
The Malt House
Brookhouse Lane
Denbigh
Clwyd
North Wales

Denbigh 2805 (STD code 074 571)

Showroom open 10am – 6pm six days. Sundays
– please telephone before coming.

Annette Fuchs   52
The Old School House
Witheridge Hill
Nr Henley on Thames
Oxon. RG9 5PF

Henley-on-Thames 641427 (STD code 0491)

Visitors welcome by appointment

Tessa Fuchs   53
Home:
24 Cross Road
Kingston upon Thames
Surrey KT2 6HG

(01) 549 6906

Studio:
26B Dunstable Road
Richmond
Surrey TW9 1VH

(01) 940 1874

Visitors welcome by appointment

Tony Gant   54
53 Southdean Gardens
Southfields
London SW19 6NT

(01) 789 4518

Trade enquiries welcomed

160

John Gibson   55
11 Meadow Terrace
Hunters Bar
Sheffield S11 8QN

Sheffield 668838 (STD code 0742)

Visitors welcome by appointment

Ian Gregory   56
The Pottery
Ansty
Nr. Dorchester
Dorset DT2 7PN

Milton Abbas 880891 (STD code 0258)

Showroom open seven days a week.
Winter 9am–5pm, Summer 9am–9pm.

Arthur J Griffiths   57
9 Loughborough Road
Walton-Le-Wolds
Leics. LE12 8HT

Wymeswold 880637 (STD code 0509)

I work alone and have no showroom, so visitors
by appointment only.

Frank Hamer   58
Llwyn-On
Croes-yn-y-Pant
Mamhilad
Pontypool
Gwent NP4 8RE

Little Mill 282 (STD code 049 528)

Visitors welcome preferably by appointment

Jane Hamlyn   59
Millfield Pottery
Everton
Nr Doncaster
S. Yorks. DN10 5DD

Retford 817 723 (STD code 0777)

Visitors welcome – telephone first if possible

Henry Hammond   60
St Maixent
Long Garden Walk
Farnham
Surrey GU9 7HX

Farnham 714564 (STD code 0252)

Studio: The Oast Pottery
Bentley, Farnham, Surrey

Visitors are welcome by appointment

Muriel Harris   61
La Fontenelle
Samares Lane
St Clement
Jersey
Channel Islands

Jersey 54226 (STD code 0534)

Workshop by telephone appointment

Alan Heaps   62
Minhafren
Aberbechan
Newtown
Powys SY16 3AW

Abermule 644 (STD code 068 686)

The workshop is open at any reasonable time

Ewen Henderson   63
4 Cliff Road
London NW1

(01) 485 5305

No visitors

Joan Hepworth   64
Westcott Pottery
Robin Cottage
Stones Lane
Westcott
Dorking
Surrey RH4 3QH

Dorking 880392 (STD code 0306)

Visitors welcome by appointment but does not
employ assistants or trainees

Thomas Howard   65
21 Connaught Avenue
Loughton
Essex IG10 4DS

(01) 508 6172

Individual thrown oxidised stoneware and
porcelain for use rather than ornament. Range
of about a dozen standard glazes. Occasional
incised decoration and sometimes slip inlay
decoration. 1953-1958 studied at local
community association evening classes.
Graduated as chemist from Cambridge. Works
for pleasure not profit as potting is a spare time
hobby.
Visitors by arrangement in limited numbers only.

Anita Hoy 66
50 Julian Avenue
London W3

(01) 992 4041

Visitors by appointment only

John Huggins 67
Courtyard Pottery
Groundwell Farm
Cricklade Road
Swindon
Wilts.

Swindon 721111 (STD code 0793)

Workshop open Monday – Saturday 10am
to 5pm

Neil Ions 68
Kitebrook Workshop
Home Farm
Kitebrook
Moreton-on-Marsh
Gloucestershire GL56 0RW

Barton-on-Heath 482 (STD code 060 874)

Visitors by appointment only

John Jelfs 69
The Pottery
Clapton Road
Bourton-on-the-Water
Gloucestershire GL54 2DN

Cotswold 20173 (STD code 0451)

Showrooms open 9am – 5.30pm most days, but
telephone call advisable if travelling long distance.

Christopher Jenkins 70
19 Towngate
Marsden
Yorkshire HD7 6DD

Huddersfield 844444 (STD code 0484)

Visitors welcome by appointment

David Lloyd Jones 71
Fulford House
45 Fulford
York YO1 4PJ

York 33331 (STD code 0904)

Showroom open daily 9am – 6pm and visitors
welcome to see workshop

Walter Keeler 72
Moorcroft Cottage
Penallt
Monmouth
Gwent NP5 4AH

Monmouth 3946 (STD code 0600)

Visitors welcome but please telephone first

Colin Kellam 73
The Lion Brewery
South Street
Totnes
Devon TQ9 5DZ

Totnes 863158 (STD code 0803)

Visitors welcome at showroom

Danny Killick 74
Waxway Farm
East Hill
Ottery St Mary
Devon EX11 1QD

Ottery St Mary 4844 (STD code 040 481)

Visitors by appointment

Ruth King 75
Fulford House
45 Fulford
York YO1 4PJ

York 33331 (STD code 0904)

Visitors welcome by appointment

Peter Lane 76
The White House
36 Keswick Road
Cringleford
Norwich NR4 6UG

Norwich 55002 (STD code 0603)

Visitors welcome by appointment only

Richard Launder 77
Studio 2
Shippon House
Cleave Hill
Dolton
Devon EX19 8QT

Dolton 440 (STD code 080 54)

Visitors welcome by appointment

David Leach   78
Lowerdown Pottery
Bovey Tracey
Devon

Bovey Tracey 833408 (STD code 0626)

Visitors are welcome at showroom 9am − 6pm
weekdays, Saturdays 9am − lpm by appointment
only.

Janet Leach   79
Leach Pottery
St Ives
Cornwall

Penzance 796398 (STD code 0736)

Showroom open Monday − Friday 9am − 5pm,
Saturday 10am − 2pm (summer only). There is
also an exhibition room of the work of Bernard
Leach.

John Leach   80
Muchelney Pottery
Muchelney
Nr Langport
Somerset TA10 0DW

Langport 250324 (STD code 0458)

Pottery Shop open Monday − Friday 9am − lpm,
2pm − 6pm. Saturday 9am − lpm. Workshop
viewing by prior arrangement. Please telephone.

Eileen Lewenstein   81
11 Western Esplanade
Portslade
Brighton
East Sussex BN4 1WE

Brighton 418705 (STD code 0273)

Visitors welcome by appointment

John Lomas   82
12 The Green
Jordans
Nr Beaconsfield
Bucks. HP9 2SU

Chalfont St Giles 4556 (STD code 02407)

Visitors by appointment only

Andrew McGarva   83
Wobage Farm
Upton Bishop
Ross-on-Wye
Herefordshire HR9 7QP

Upton Bishop 233 (STD code 098 985)

Visitors welcome at the showroom by
appointment. Please telephone first if possible

Mal Magson   84
'The Old Swan'
32 Main Street
East Ayton
Scarborough
North Yorks. YO13 9HL

Scarborough 863463 (STD code 0723)

Visitors (in small numbers) welcome by
appointment

John Maltby   85
Stoneshill Pottery
Stoneshill
Crediton
Devon

Crediton 2753 (STD code 036 32)

Visitors welcome at any reasonable time (not
Sundays). Please telephone first if making a
special journey from a distance.

Victor Margrie   86
3 The Polygon
Clifton
Bristol BS8 4PW

Bristol 277 527 (STD code 0272)

Setting up pottery

West Marshall   87
Spring Lodge
Mundford Road
Methwold
Thetford
Norfolk IP26 4RN

Methwold 728826
(STD code 0366)

Born 1945 in Middlesex. Trained at Harrow School of Art 1961-65 and gained the Art Teachers Diploma at Bristol in 1966. Taught two days a week at the Harrow Studio Pottery course since 1967. Worked in Whittington, Norfolk 1970-81. Moved to Methwold 1982. Currently producing small quantities of decorative functional porcelain, often pierced and with enamel on-glaze colours. Exhibitions: Atmosphere, London 1976; Bohun Gallery, Henley 1977; King's Lynn Museum 1978; Studio 10½, Hull 1979. Visitors by appointment.

Leo Francis Matthews   88
Ivy Court Mews
Shawbury
Salop.

Shawbury 250 866 (STD code 0939)

Visitors by appointment only

Peter Meanley   89
6 Downshire Road
Bangor
Co. Down BT20 3TW

Bangor 466831 (STD code 0247)

Visitors are welcome by appointment

Eric James Mellon   90
5 Parkfield Avenue
Bognor Regis
West Sussex PO21 3BW

Pagham 263221 (STD code 0243)

Clients by appointment

David Miller   91
33 St Andrew's Square
Surbiton
Surrey KT6 4EG

(01) 399 2698

Viewing by prior arrangement

David Morris   92
Biergate Cottage
Main Road
Grainthorpe
Louth
Lincolnshire LN11 7HX

Marshchapel 260 (STD code 047 286)

Visitors welcome by appointment

Bryan Newman   93
The Pottery
Aller
Langport
Somerset TA10 0QN

Langport 250 244 (STD code 0458)

Visitors welcome dawn till dusk, Monday – Friday. If we are in Saturday and Sunday we are open, but ring to avoid disappointment.

Eileen Nisbet   94
25 Millman Street
London WC1N 3EP

(01) 242 7362

Magdalene Anyango N Odundo   95
Workshop:
5 The Pollards
Alton Road
Bentley
Hants. GU10 5NE

Home:
Bentley 22560 (STD code 0420)

Messages can be left on the answering machine

Warwick Parker   96
The Dairy House
Maiden Newton
Dorchester
Dorset

Maiden Newton 20414 (STD code 0300)

Opening hours of showroom and workshop are between 9am and 5pm Monday to Friday, 9am to 12 noon Saturday. Please telephone if coming from a long distance.

Colin Pearson   97
3 Mountfort Terrace
Barnsbury Square
Islington
London N1 1JJ

(01) 607 1965

Studio and Showroom:
15-17 Cloudesley Road
London N1

Visitors welcome by appointment. 5 minutes
Angel underground. Easy parking.

Anthony Phillips   98
Postal address:
21 Henry House
Coin Street
London SE1 8YE

Workshop address:
3rd Floor
O & N Warehouse
Metropolitan Wharf
Wapping Wall
London E1

(01) 481 3440

Visitors welcome by appointment

Peter Phillips   99
Ivy Cottage
Taylors Lane
Trottiscliffe
Kent ME19 5DS

Fairseat 822901 (STD code 0732)

Henry Pim   100
98 Railton Road
London SE24

(01) 274 2246

Visitors welcome by appointment

Ian Pirie   101
8 St Michael's Road
Newtonhill
Stonehaven
Kincardineshire

Stonehaven 30908 (STD code 0569)

Visitors by appointment

John Pollex   102
Barbican Craft Workshops
1 White Lane
Barbican
Plymouth PL1 2LP

Plymouth 662338 (STD code 0752)

Showroom is open to the public throughout the
year 9am – 5pm. Visitors to the workshop can
do so by appointment.

Vicki Read   103
"Claycutters"
Sheep Street
Winslow
Buckingham MK18 3HN

Winslow 2663 (STD code 029 671)

Showroom on the premises

Stanislas Reychan   104
757 The White House
Albany Street
London NW1 3UP

(01) 387 1200

Mary Rich   105
Penwerris Pottery
Cowlands Creek
Old Kea
Nr Truro
Cornwall TR3 6AT

Truro 76926 (STD code 0872)

Visitors are welcome at my workshop by prior
arrangement

Christine-Ann Richards   106
14a Percy Circus
London WC1X 9ES

(01) 833 1898

Visitors to studio by appointment only. Work
for sale.

David Roberts   107
Cressfield House
44 Upperthong Lane
Holmfirth
Huddersfield
West Yorkshire HD7 1BQ

Huddersfield 685110 (STD code 0484)

No showroom but visitors are welcome to
workshop by appointment

James W Robison   108
Booth House Gallery
3 Booth House
Holmfirth
Huddersfield
West Yorkshire HD7 1QA

Huddersfield 6852 70 (STD code 0484)

Studio and Gallery open weekends and by
appointment

Mary Rogers   109
Brook Farm House
Nanpantan Road
Loughborough
Leics. LE11 3YE

Loughborough 239205 (STD code 0509)

No showroom. The work is sold through
exhibitions and galleries.

Phil Rogers   110
Marston Pottery
Lower Cefn Faes
Rhayader, Powys

Rhayader 810875 (STD code 0597)

also at Bridge Street, Rhayader.

Visitors are welcome at the workshop at any
reasonable time

David Scott   111
33 Cross Lane
Mountsorrel
Leicester LE12 7BU

Leicester 302100 (STD code 0533)

Visitors welcome by appointment

Ray Silverman   112
35 Dunster Crescent
Hornchurch, Essex

Hornchurch 58864 (STD code 040 24)

Visitors by appointment

Michael Skipwith   113
Lotus Pottery
Stoke Gabriel
Totnes
S. Devon TQ9 6SL

Stoke Gabriel 303 (STD code 080 428)

Workshop and showroom open Monday to
Friday 9am – 5.30pm and usually on Saturday
mornings 9am – 1pm.

Mildred Slatter   114
The White Cottage
Framewood Road
Stoke Poges SL2 4QR

Fulmer 3249 (STD code 028 16)

Visitors are welcome to the studio and
showroom at any time, but please telephone
beforehand.

Frank Smith   115
Old Winders House
Peasmarsh
Rye
Sussex TN31 6YJ

Peasmarsh 284 (STD code 079 721)

House easily found on A268 four miles from
Rye. Visitors at any reasonable time.

Peter Smith   116
Bojewyan Pottery
Higher Bojewyan
Pendeen
Penzance
Cornwall TR19 7TR

Penzance 788820 (STD code 0736)

Visitors welcome at any reasonable time

John Solly   117
36 London Road
Maidstone
Kent ME16 8QL

Maidstone 54623 (STD code 0622)

Sells work direct from pottery

Gary Standige   118
500 Station Road
Aylesford
Kent

Maidstone 70730 (STD code 0622)

Visitors welcome by a prior telephone call

Peter Starkey   119
Pine Cottage
Great Doward
Symonds Yat
Nr Ross-on-Wye
Herefordshire HR9 6BP

Symonds Yat 89 0823 (STD code 0600)

Visitors by appointment

Peter Stoodley   120
Workshop:
15 Gordon Road
Boscombe
Bournemouth
Dorset BH1 4DW

Bournemouth 36766 (STD code 0202)

View by appointment

Warren and Debora Storch   121
Lawers Farm Pottery
Comrie
Perthshire PH6 2LT

Comrie 70207 (STD code 0764)

Visitors welcome by appointment

Harry Horlock Stringer   122
Taggs Yard School of Ceramics
11½ Woodlands Road
Barnes
London SW13 0JZ

(01) 876 5750

Visits arranged by telephone appointments only

Helen Swain   123
8 Fyfield Road
Waltham Forest
London E17 3RG

(01) 520 4043

This is a one woman pottery, at home, so visitors by appointment and, sorry, no students possible at present.

Geoffrey Swindell   124
35 Murch Road
Dinas Powis
Cardiff CF6 4RD

Cardiff 512746 (STD code 0222)

I see purchasing visitors only and by appointment

Janice Tchalenko   125
30 Therapia Road
London SE22

(01) 693 1624

Visitors by appointment only

Sabina Teuteberg   126
c/o C.P.A.
William Blake House
7 Marshall Street
London W1V 1FD

(01) 437 7605

Owen Thorpe   127
Churchstoke Pottery
Churchstoke
Powys SY15 6AG

Churchstoke 511 (STD code 058 85)

Visitors welcome by appointment

Vera Tollow   128
5 Woodcote Mews
Wallington
Surrey SM6 8RB

(01) 647 9898

Visitors are welcome by appointment only

Marianne de Trey   129
Shinners Bridge Pottery
Dartington
Totnes
Devon TQ9 6JB

Totnes 862046 (STD code 0803) (after 6pm)

Visitors preferably by appointment

Angela Verdon   130
Gladstone Pottery Museum
Uttoxeter Road
Longton
Stoke-on-Trent
Staffs.

Stoke-on-Trent 319232 (STD code 0782)

I have a showroom and welcome visitors by appointment only

Alan Wallwork   131
"Abbotsford"
Woodhouse Hill
Uplyme, Lyme Regis
Dorset DT7 3SL

Lyme Regis 2756 (STD code 029 74)

Visitors are welcome but not too early. A prior phone call helps, especially as advice on access should avoid getting lost in the lanes.

Sarah Walton   132
Keepers
Selmeston
Nr Polegate
Sussex BN26 6UH

Ripe 517 and 284 (STD code 032 183)

Visitors welcome to showroom especially those
who telephone beforehand

John Ward   133
Fachongle Uchaf
Cilgwyn
Newport
Dyfed SA42 0QR

Newport 820 706 (STD code 0239)

Visitors by appointment

Sasha Wardell   134
Lutsey Farm Cottage
Worton
Devizes
Wiltshire

Seend 528 (STD code 0380 82)

Visitors by appointment

Robin Welch   135
Robin Welch Pottery
Stradbroke
Diss
Norfolk

Stradbroke 416 (STD code 037 984)

Visitors welcome 10am – 6pm Monday to
Saturday

Tony Weston   136
Little Cokenach
Nuthampstead
Royston
Herts.

Barkway 464 (STD code 076 384)

Visitors welcome by appointment

John Wheeldon   137
Wheatsheaf House
Church Street
Matlock
Derbyshire

Matlock 55975 (STD code 0629)

Resident but please telephone

Mary White   138
Zimmerplatzweg 6
6551 Wonsheim
B.R.D.

06703/2922

Visitors welcome, but better telephone first

Geoffrey Whiting   139
2 Monastery Street
Canterbury
Kent CT1 1NJ

Canterbury 457064 (STD code 0227)

Visitors are welcome by appointment

Caroline Whyman   140
15 Swan Yard
Highbury Station Road
London N1 1SD

(01) 226 9403

Visitors are welcome to call during the day, but
please telephone first for directions.

David Winkley   141
Yellow Pottery
Lower Vellow
Williton
Taunton
Somerset TA4 4LS

Stogumber 56458 (STD code 0984)

The workshop and pottery shop are open to
visitors from 8.30am until 6pm Monday to
Saturday

Mollie Winterburn   142
Tancnwch
Ystradmeurig
Dyfed SY25 6AB

Pontrhydfendigaid 275 (STD code 097 45)

Mary Wondrausch   143
Wharf Pottery
Brickfields
Compton
Guildford
Surrey GU3 1HZ

Godalming 4097 (STD code 048 68)

Mon.-Fri. 9am–5pm; Sat. and Sun. 2–5pm.

Nigel Wood 144
28 Hyde Street
Winchester
Hampshire

Winchester 55463 (STD code 0962)

(Home address)

Rosemary Wren 145
The Oxshott Pottery
Mill Cottage
Mill Lane
Lustleigh
Newton Abbot
Devon TQ13 9SS

Lustleigh 231 (STD code 06477)

Works in partnership with Peter Crotty. Visitors are welcome at the studio but please telephone first if making a special journey. Lustleigh is one mile west of the A382, three miles north of Bovey Tracey − turn off A38 fifteen miles west of Exeter.

Muriel P Wright 146
Ashanwell
Potkins Lane
Orford
Woodbridge
Suffolk IP12 2SS

Woodbridge 450 580 (STD code 0394)

Trained at Manchester College of Art. Founder member of Craftsmen Potters Association. Makes fountains and pots for the garden, thrown and handbuilt. Visitors welcome but telephone call essential.

Takeshi Yasuda 147
38 East Street
South Molton
Devon EX36 3DF

South Molton 2829 (STD code 076 95)

Currently Craftsman-in-Residence 1984-1986
Cleveland Crafts Centre
57 Gilkes Street
Middlesbrough
Cleveland TS1 5EL

Middlesbrough 226351 (STD code 0642)

Joanna and Andrew Young 148
A & J Young Pottery
Common Farm
Sustead Road
Lower Gresham
Norfolk NR11 8RE

Matlaske 548 (STD code 026 377)

Have a small showroom, open on weekday mornings. All other times must be arranged by telephone.

Monica Young 149
Old Butcher's Yard
Reeth
Richmond
N. Yorks.

Richmond 84 487 (STD code 0748)

Visitors by appointment

So You Want to be a Potter

Pottery Training in the United Kingdom

The opportunities for learning pottery vary from full-time study at art school to teaching yourself from books. In this section all the possibilities are detailed under different headings.

Workshop Training

Because of the very diverse nature of craft pottery no formal apprenticeship scheme exists for training prospective potters. The kind of work undertaken by trainees, and the amount and quality of the teaching they receive in the workshop, will depend largely on the skill and outlook of the potter they work for.

Joining a workshop is not always easy. The number of potters employing assistants is small, demand for places often exceeds supply, and competition is, therefore, fierce. Success in finding a potter to work with will require a high level of commitment, strong perseverance and almost certainly some measure of luck.

You can try to join a pottery direct as a trainee assistant or for a period of workshop practice following an art school ceramics course. One with a strong bias towards craft pottery would be an advantage.

The work of some potters is so individual that it precludes additional help. Those who do employ assistants often spend much of their time making repetition ware decorative or functional. Students leaving art schools for workshops may find the change constricting. Much of the learning will inevitably be done by making pots designed initially by the teacher and the opportunities for personal expression are likely to be limited.

There are no standard rates of pay for trainees and remuneration will be set by potters according to their means and in relation to the real productive help that an assistant can give. It is the experience of many potters that students often overestimate their ability to make pots quickly and of a saleable quality. The Crafts Council offer a variety of Training Grant Schemes. Some are intended for established craftworkers and these are a great help in supplementing the wages of trainees. But this scheme is not automatically available to every potter with assistants and it must be assumed that rates of pay for trainees will be less — and in some cases considerably less — than those in industry or teaching.

The names and addresses of full members of the Craftsmen Potters Association are listed in this book. Many other potters are included in the 'Visitors Guide to Country Workshops' published by the Council for Small Industries in Rural Areas (CoSira).

Application to Workshops

Before applying to workshops see the work of as many potters as you can so that you are clear about the kind of pots you want to make. If, for example, your main interest is ceramic sculpture you are likely to be happier working with a potter whose prime interest this is than one preoccupied with domestic ware.
This obvious fact is often ignored and too few applicants apply to potters with whose work they are familiar and sympathetic.

Just writing a letter which says, in essence, 'I am interested in pottery. Do you have a job?' is unlikely to gain a positive response. Potters get many such letters from applicants who appear to post a dozen or so at a time to widely differing potters in the hope that something will turn up. It rarely does.

The better, and probably only, way is to go and see the potters of your choice in their workshops. This requires a lot of effort, it's time-consuming and demands perseverance mentioned earlier. But in seeking a workshop place you are, in effect, asking potters to make a commitment to you in time, energy and money. Potters have livings to earn and they must be as sure as they can that you are really serious about working with them to mutual advantage. In short they have to be convinced that there is something in it for them as well as you.

Before you visit, telephone or write to see that it is convenient. Take with you any examples or photographs of pots you have made. Without some evidence it is very difficult for potters to judge an applicant's ability or potential.

Working successfully and harmoniously as a member of a small team, or in conjunction with an individual potter, is as much a question of good personal relationships as the teaching and acquisition of skills. In the search for workshop places, therefore, it is difficult to overestimate the value of personal contact. This works both ways: it enables potters to judge at first hand an applicant's response to the work they do and, equally important, it gives applicants the opportunity to see what facilities are available and to say what they can offer the workshop. Trainees have much to give in enthusiasm for and commitment to working with clay, and in ready willingness to share all the many and sometimes tedious jobs that every workshop has to undertake to produce finished pots.

Full-time courses in art colleges and polytechnics

Graduate level courses BA(Hons)

These three or four year Courses preceded by a one or two year Foundation Course aim for the development of the individual rather than his/her training for a specific employment situation. Entry is highly competitive and educational requirements stringent (usually 5 GCE 'O' level passes, although some colleges demand one or two 'A' level passes). Pottery (Ceramics) is usually contained in three dimensional design 'area' and courses include compulsory work in other media and a proportion of Art History and Complementary Studies. In the Colleges offering Ceramics as a 'chief study' the emphasis varies widely between the poles of the craft, fine-art and industrial design pottery, though most make opportunities for all these in some degree. Intending students should study prospectuses or visit courses before making applications.

For residents in the UK grants for these courses are mandatory, once a place has been secured, but are subject to means test and other certain conditions. Overseas students may have to pay full fees and satisfy interviewing boards that they are financially viable.

Vocational courses and BTEC

These courses differ from the above in these respects:

● The entry requirements are usually less stringent.

● The courses are geared more towards professional training for subsequent employment as technician, craftworker, designer/craftworker or designer.

● Grants are at the discretion of the LEAs.

● Courses vary from 2–4 years.

● Courses, which usually lead to a local, regional or professional Diploma or Licentiateship include some ancillary studies in drawing, design and other craft techniques.

No official 'sandwich' courses for studio potters exist at present but some Colleges make informal arrangements for students to work in potters' workshops during the course or in vacations.

Colleges offering full-time courses in ceramics

	College	Course, entry requirements & qualifications and description of course supplied by college
ENGLAND		
Amersham	**Amersham College of Further Education and Art** Stanley Hill, Amersham Bucks HP7 9HN Tel: Amersham 21121 (STD code 024 03)	Vocational Course, 2 years Regional diploma
Birmingham	**City of Birmingham Polytechnic Art & Design Centre** New Corporation Street Birmingham B4 7DX Tel: Birmingham 359 6721 (STD code 021)	BA(Hons) 3D design CNAA ceramics with gla 1 year foundation 5 'O's. 18+
Bournemouth	**Bournemouth and Poole College of Art and Design** Wallisdown Road, Poole Dorset BH12 5HH Tel: Bournemouth 533011 (STD code 0202)	Specialist option BTEC General Art and Design Diploma
Brighton	**Brighton Polytechnic Faculty of Art and Design** Grand Parade, Brighton BN2 2JY Tel: Brighton 604141 (STD code 0273)	BA(Hons) CNAA – wood, metal, ceramics and plastics course. 3 years full time. Normally 1 year foundation + 5 'O's Direct entry 2 'A's + 3 'O's.
Bristol	**Bristol Polytechnic Faculty of Art and Design** Clanage Road, Bower Ashton Bristol BS3 2JU Tel: Bristol 660222 (STD code 0272)	BA(Hons) Ceramics. The course provides a broad and divergent experience of ceramics; established techniques and approaches are studied, forming the basis for independent development. Drawing and the creation of two dimensional work is of equal importance with the making of artifacts. The projects – terms one to five – are designed stimulate interest in a wide experience of techniques and materials, in design considerations, and in personal expression. This evolves into an individual, self-directed programme of work in the final year.

Carlisle	**Cumbria College of Art & Design** Brampton Road, Carlisle Cumbria CA3 9AY Tel: Carlisle 25333 (STD code 0228)	BTEC HND. Design Crafts. Successful applicants can choose three out of ten options which are:- Fabric Printing, Weaving, Knitting, Embroidery, Throwing with Decorative Processes, Throwing with Pressmoulding, Craft Related Industrial Ceramics, Surface Decoration in Ceramics and Multi-Media Studies. The course, therefore, offers a vocational training for both mainstream craftspeople and for those looking for multi-discipline possibilities. With the intention of setting up their workshops, students are fully supported in essential business, historical and technical areas and by lectures and demonstrations by established crafts people.
Colchester	**North Essex School of Art Colchester Institute** Sheepen Road, Colchester Essex CO3 3LL Tel: Colchester 570271 (STD code 0206)	East Anglian Regional Advisory Council Diploma in Applied Art and Design
Corsham	**Bath College of Education** *(until September 1986)* Corsham Court, Corsham, Wiltshire Tel: Corsham 712571 (STD code 0249) *After September 1986:* **Bath College of Higher Education** Faculty of Art and Music Sion Hill Place, Lansdown Bath BA1 5SJ Tel: Bath 25264 (STD code 0255)	BA(Hons) Ceramics
Derby	**Derbyshire College of Higher Education** Kedleston Road, Derby DE3 1GB Tel: Derby 47181 (STD code 0332)	BTEC National Diploma in Studio Ceramics. Qualifications necessary: National Diploma in Design Crafts, General Art and Design or General Vocational Design (National Diploma). Successful completion of a Foundation Course. Exceptional case entry may be from 6th Form or for mature students with alternative professional qualifications. Students accepted on the course are eligible for mandatory awards.
Eastbourne	**College of Arts and Technology** St. Anne's Road, Eastbourne Sussex BN21 2HS Tel: Eastbourne 644711 (STD code 0323)	16+. BTEC General Vocational Design Diploma. (3 'O'/CSE 1) and BTEC General Art and Design Diploma. (5 'O'/CSE 1) 2 year courses with Ceramics as a Specialist Design Option. Post Diploma. Vocational Studio Ceramics. A practical 2 year course leading to Dip.SIAD and LSD-C.
Epsom	**Epsom School of Art & Design** Ashley Road, Epsom, Surrey KT18 5BE Tel: Epsom 28811 (STD code 03727)	2 year BTEC National Diploma 2 year BTEC Higher National Diploma in Design Crafts.

Exeter	**Exeter College of Art & Design** Earl Richards Road North Exeter EX2 6AS Tel: Exeter 77977 (STD code 0392)	BA(Hons) Course in Fine Art. The work in this area of study is assessed through Fine Art standards and not those normally associated with craft base design activities. A broad range of experience in materials, methods, scale and concepts is provided and the general aims are those of the Fine Art Department as a whole. Consideration is given to the special nature of any study, e.g. a student wishing to specialise in large-scale ceramic sculptures would acquire appropriate knowledge of studio organisation, clays and glazes and firing techniques that would be suitable for this study. Emphasis is invariably placed on individual creativity covering both 2-D and 3-D work: no conventional line is drawn between these dimensions. The ceramic studios are large and well equipped. Most ceramic techniques and materials are available and large-scale work is encouraged.
Farnham	**West Surrey College of Art and Design** The Hart, Farnham, Surrey Tel: Farnham 722441 (STD code 025 12)	BA(Hons) Ceramics with supporting studies. The practice of Studio Ceramics provides the core discipline for this chief study. Students study a wide range of methods of forming and decorating ceramics; handbuilding, pressing and wheelforming, modelling and mould forming, the decorative techniques involved these processes, and the various fabrics and finishing methods appropriate to them. From this wide range of techniques students are actively encouraged to experiment and explore bringing their own enthusiasms to their work. The very broad range of facilities offered allows for both a traditional approach to the medium or a more innovative handling of ceramics. The Workshops are exceptionally well equipped with over 30 kilns, large clay preparation and glazing facilities and extensive studios and workshops.
Harrogate	**Harrogate College of Arts & Adult Studies** 2 Victoria Avenue Harrogate HG1 1EL Tel: Harrogate 62446 (STD code 0423)	BTEC National Diploma Course in Studio Ceramics. The Course is intended to ensure that students will develop as skilled creative artists whilst, at the same time, acquiring the appropriate technical knowledge concerning the processes of manufacture. In order to achieve this there are three main areas of study: Practical Skills; Technical Understanding; and Two-dimensional Design and Drawing Skills. The programme is highly structured to develop by means of exploration and experimentation of the practical possibilities of clay, its firing temperature and glaze qualities. Students work a block project system which explores major areas of ceramic production. Part-time Ceramic Training. This runs alongside the full-time programme for a limited number of students who may only be able to attend three days per week, but seek

the opportunity of studying in depth over a three-year period. We encourage applications from mature students.

Hereford	**Hereford College of Art and Design** Folly Lane, Hereford Tel: Hereford 273359 (STD code 0432)	BTEC National Diploma in Art and Design College Higher Diploma in Small Studio Practice

High Wycombe   **Buckinghamshire College of Higher Education School of Art & Design**
Queen Alexandra Road
High Wycombe HP11 2JZ
Tel: High Wycombe 22141
(STD code 0494)

BA(Hons) Ceramics with glass. This exciting new course provides a broad-based experience of working with both clay and glass, and students are taught both studio and industrial crafts skills. The aim of the course is to help students develop a personal and visual awareness through working with these materials, thus providing a sound basis for their future development as artists and designers. Project work is designed to encourage students to consider a wide range of possible applications of both glass and ceramics. The department has recently acquired new well designed facilities and enjoys the latest technology and equipment. The course is well staffed, and is unique in the range of staff skills it can call upon within the college.

Leicester   **Leicester Polytechnic School of Industrial Design**
P.O. Box 143, Leicester LE1 9BH
Tel: Leicester 551551
(STD code 0533)

Full time BA(Hons) 3D ceramics (glass)
A three year full-time course leading to a BA(Hons) Degree in 3 Dimensional Design. In the first year all work is carried out through set projects that involve both industrial and studio processes using clay, plaster and glass, kiln firing and construction, photography, drawing and decoration, as well as wide ranging lectures concerning Theoretical Studies, History of Art and Associated Studies. In the second year, individual projects are agreed between students and the year tutor. An industrial project is tackled, usually in the form of a national bursary competition. Technical information, Group Seminars, History of Ceramics and Glass and a choice of Associated Studies topics complement studio work. Student exchanges in Europe and USA are encouraged during this year. In the final year agreed projects range from individual ideas exploring personal dreams and fantasies through to production tableware and giftware. Well equipped workshops and knowledgeable academic and technical staff are available to help you to achieve the highest standards. Regular visits take place to studios, factories, exhibitions, museums and places of interest.

London	**Camberwell School of Art & Crafts** Peckham Road, London SE5 8UF Tel: 01-703-0987	BA(Hons) ceramics LSIA 3 year course. Normal method of entry at 18+ is from a Foundation course, but exceptions may be made depending on experience and ability. The course, which is largely staffed by practising potters and sculptors, offers a broadly based approach to the making of objects both functional and sculptural in fire clay. The development of the student's personal vision is considered to be importan and to this end the students are encouraged to draw and to keep visual notebooks.
	Central School of Art & Design Southampton Row London WC1B 4AP Tel: 01-405-1825	BA(Hons) ceramics LSIA. The Department provides a three-year full-time course leadin to the BA(Hons) degree. It also offers a few places to students who wish to undertake advanced studies leading to the CSAD Diploma. The BA course is intended for applicants who show evidence of a high degree of creative potential and who are strongly motivated to work in the field of ceramics. The course aims to ensure that its students will develop their creative and intellectual powers and acquire skills, knowledge and judgement commensurate with professional practice.
	Roehampton Institute of Higher Education Roehampton Lane London SW15 5PJ Tel: 01-878-5751	Degree Course in art (including pottery).
(Greater London)	**Barnet College** Wood Street, Barnet, Herts EN5 4AZ Tel: 01-440-6321	BTEC General Diploma in Art & Design Pre-degree Foundation Course in Art and Design.
	Croydon College Fairfield, Croydon CR9 1DX Tel: 02-688-9271	2 year BTEC National Higher Diploma in Ceramics. The course aims to train designers and crafts people who can use bo hand and industrial methods in the product of ceramic wares for current and future markets. Techniques of making are primaril concerned with creating individual products a specialised character for limited scale production, one-offs and commissioned works.
	Harrow College of Higher Education Northwick Park, Harrow HA1 3TP Tel: 01-864-5422	2 years BTEC Higher Diploma, LSD-C. Entr appropriate DATEC Diploma or Certificate Foundation or equivalent. The two year vocational course at Harrow has probably trained more practising potters than any ot course. Currently offering a BTEC Higher Diploma in Studio Pottery, the course cover most methods of hand manufacture, a varie of firing methods and a comprehensive rang of decorative techniques. Taking function as the basis for study, the course aims to explo

through drawing, throwing, hand building, technology and written research each student's skills, invention, imagination and individuality.

Hounslow Borough College
London Road, Isleworth
Middlesex TW7 4HS
Tel: 01-568-0244

Foundation course 1 year 5 'O' levels BTEC Diploma General Art and Design 2 years. 4 'O' levels 3D Design

Middlesex Polytechnic
Cat Hill, Barnet
Herts. EN4 8HT
Tel: 01-440-5181

BA(Hons) 3D Design/Ceramics 3yrs 5 'O's, 3 'O's + 1 'A', 2 'O's + 2 'A's, or 3 'A's providing there is evidence other subjects have been taken. BA(Hons) Jewellery/Ceramics. 4 yrs which includes 1 year sandwich placement. On the BA 3D course first year all students have an opportunity to work across a wide range of materials and techniques, the chief study areas of ceramics, furniture and metal and glass, plastic, fabric, C.A.D. The emphasis is on individual development and the second and third years continue this in ceramic terms. The whole range of ceramic work is equally encouraged. BAJ/C Ceramics students specialise from the start, undergoing an intensive technical instruction during the first year and developing personal directions through projects during the second. Emphasis is on functional ware of both craft and industrial flavour. The area is exceptionally well equipped to deal with both aspects. Placement in working situations during the third year is geared to individual needs and the fourth year is non-project based, students developing their individual directions.

Ravensbourne College of Art & Design
Walden Road, Chislehurst
Kent BR7 5SN
Tel: 01-468-7071

BA(Hons) Wood/metal/plastics/ceramics

Loughborough

Loughborough College of Art & Design
Radmoor, Loughborough, Leicestershire
Tel: Loughborough 261515
(STD code 0509)

BA(Hons) ceramics

Lowestoft

Lowestoft School of Art College of Further Education
St. Peters Street, Lowestoft
Suffolk NR32 2NB
Tel: Lowestoft 85321
(STD code 0502)

BTEC Ordinary National Diploma (2 years) Certificate of Institute of Ceramics (3 years) East Anglian Diploma (3 years) + 1 year to CIC, DSIAD

Manchester	**Manchester Polytechnic Faculty of Art & Design**	BA(Hons) 3D Design wood/metal/ceramics/ glass. A multi-disciplinary course offering
	Cavendish Street, All Saints	Ceramics as a main option. The course
	Manchester MI5 6BR	covers Studio, Industrial, Architectural
	Tel: Manchester 228 6171	and Fine Art ceramics leading in the third year
	(STD code 061)	to a more individually orientated expression.
		Career possibilities: further study at MA level
		the teaching profession (including C.D.T.),
		Designing for industry, setting up small
		businesses and workshops, working as artist
		potters. Included in the course are Visual
		Studies (Drawing), History of Art and Design
		Liberal Studies, Business and Professional
		Studies.

Middlesbrough	**Cleveland College of Art & Design**	College Certificate in Design Crafts (Ceramics) 3 years part-time, BTEC National
	Green Lane, Middlesbrough	Diploma in General Art and Design/
	Cleveland	Foundation Course (Ceramics Option) full
	Tel: Middlesbrough 821441	time 1 and 2 yrs. The course offers personal
	(STD code 0642)	development in both the techniques and
		aesthetics of contemporary studio ceramics.

Nuneaton	**North Warwickshire College of Technology & Art**	BTEC National Diploma in Three Dimensional Design Ceramics. A full-time
	Hinckley Road, Nuneaton	2 year course designed for students interested
	Warwickshire CVII 6BH	in a professional career as a
	Tel: Nuneaton 349321	designer/craftsman/technician in Ceramics.
	(STD code 0203)	The aim is to provide students with the skills
		and knowledge necessary for continued
		further education or employment, enabling
		them to follow a career related to their
		interests and skills in the design studio of a
		factory, the ceramic workshop or studio
		pottery. The course is intended to ensure that
		students will develop as skilled
		artists/craftsmen and at the same time acquire
		the appropriate knowledge related to the
		commercial aspects of ceramics.

Preston	**Lancashire Polytechnic Faculty of Art & Design**	Higher National Diploma (Three Dimensional Design). The course provides an opportunity
	Preston PRI 2TQ	for students to study a wide range of craft
	Tel: Preston 22141	processes and develop skills and sensibilities
	(STD code 0772)	appropriate to employment as a designer-
		craftsman working in a small independent
		workshop or craft centre; a product
		development department in mass production
		industry; as a craft assistant in an educational,
		social services, recreational organisation. The
		distinctive feature of the course is the
		provision for integrating the attitudes and
		techniques associated with both one-off and
		volume production and for developing an
		individual style and range of design and
		craftwork which is both personally satisfying
		and appropriate to a wide range of vocational
		possibilities.

Redruth	**Cornwall College of Further & Higher Education** Redruth, Cornwall Tel: Camborne 712911 (STD code 0209)	BTEC National Diploma in General Vocational Design (2 years) BTEC Higher National Diploma Ceramics (2 years)
Rochester	**Medway College of Design** Fort Pitt, Rochester Kent MEI IDZ Tel: Medway 44815 (STD code 0634)	2 year Higher National Diploma in Design Ceramics. Normally 16 years + 3 'O' levels. 2 year Higher Diploma Course Design Crafts Ceramics. Normally 18 years + 5 'O' levels The course aims to equip students with the knowledge and skills to start a workshop and practice as a studio potter, making domestic ware or individual ware in either a traditional way or with new and modern concepts. The syllabus provides thorough guidance and practice in the skills of making and decorating pottery of all types, whether handbuilt, thrown, or cast and provides a working knowledge of the commercial aspects of running a workshop. National Diploma in Design. Option in Ceramics 2 years. Entry requirements: minimum age 16 years, minimum 3 G.C.E. O levels or equivalent plus evidence of art/craft/design study. The course includes a wide range of visual studies including drawing, painting and designing and complementary studies which encourages interest in the historical, social, economical and philosophical aspects of the craft. Familiarity with all techniques is essential including handbuilding, throwing and turning and mouldmaking, using earthenware, stoneware and porcelain. Students pack and fire their own kilns and they can build their own kiln if they wish, and they can also construct their own power wheel or kick wheel. Most students wish to go on to Higher Education but others start their own workshops or go as assistants.
Rotherham	*(From Sept.1986)* **Rotherham College of Arts and Technology** Eastwood Lane Rotherham, South Yorks. Tel: Rotherham 362111 (STD code 0709)	BTEC National Diploma Course Ceramics Design and Technology
Stafford	**Stafford College of Further Education** Earl Street, Stafford Staffordshire ST16 2QR Tel: Stafford 42361 (STD code 0785)	Foundation Course in Art and Design
Stoke-on-Trent	**North Staffordshire Polytechnic** Department of Design (Ceramics) College Road Stoke on Trent ST4 2DE Tel: Stoke on Trent 45531 (STD code 0782)	BA(Hons) Design, multi-disciplinary design course including specialisation in Industrial Ceramics, Hand Pottery, Ceramic Sculpture, Glass. This is a main subject specialisation within the course structure of the Multi-disciplinary Design Course providing the

opportunity for the easy "cross fertilisation" with other related subject areas such as surface pattern, glassmaking, domestic product design etc. The programme provide a broad practical ceramic design education leading to specialisation in the third and fina year in industrial or studio based work. BTE Higher National Diploma Design (Ceramics A two year programme of full time study aimed at producing assistant designers and design technicians capable of working in Industry or smaller manufacturing units. Students specialise in their second year in either design for shape or decoration.

Stourbridge	**Stourbridge College of Technology & Art** Hagley Road, Stourbridge West Midlands DY8 1QU Tel: Stourbridge 78531 (STD code 038 43)	BA(Hons) 3D Design, Glass with ceramics
Wolverhampton	**The Polytechnic Wolverhampton Faculty of Art & Design** Molineux Street Wolverhampton WV1 1SB Tel: Wolverhampton 898176 (STD code 0902)	BA(Hons) ceramics LSD-C. The aim of the course is to enable each student to develop a personal creative response to a wide varie of ceramic materials and techniques. Additionally there are facilities to undertake supportive work in wood, metal, plastics, photography, and computer usage. There is also a programme of kiln building with a variety of firing processes. The ceramics department also has its own printing workshop. The 1st year is an induction exploratory year where students work in a variety of media and techniques to develop craft skills. The 2nd year achieves a balance between set projects and personally motivated work, whilst the 3rd year aims to consolidate personal creative motives with professional expertise.

WALES

Cardiff	**South Glamorgan Institute of Higher Education Faculty of Art & Design** Howard Gardens, Cardiff CF2 1SP Tel: Cardiff 551111 (STD code 0222)	BA(Hons) Ceramics
Carmarthen	**Carmarthenshire College of Technology & Art** Faculty of Art & Design Job's Well Road Carmarthen, Dyfed Tel: Carmarthen 233995 (STD code 0267)	BTEC National Diploma in Design (Multi-disciplinary course with a specialist option in ceramics) 2 years: Entry 3 'O's HND Diploma in Design Crafts (with a specialist option in ceramics) 2 years: Entry BTEC Diploma or Certification or Foundation Course

Newport

Gwent College of Higher Education Faculty Art & Design
College Crescent, Caerleon
Newport, Gwent NP6 IXJ
Tel: Newport 421292 (STD code 0633)

BA(Hons) Fine Art

Wrexham

NE Wales Inst Higher Education College of Art & Design
49 Regent Street
Wrexham, Clwyd
Tel: Wrexham 365955
(STD code 0978)

2 year BTEC Diploma in Studio Ceramics. The aim of the Ceramic Course is to give each student a sound understanding of the traditional materials, processes and tools of the craft. The course is essentially practical, based upon a project system and directed towards employment in the field of studio pottery. Studio ceramic technology, business studies, design history and draughtsmanship form a very important part of the course. 2 year BTEC Higher Diploma in Design Crafts. Ceramics is a major option of this course and is devised to develop a command of a full range of craft production skills related to throwing, hand building, modelling and mouldmaking. Students broaden experience and knowledge through a programme of related studies in other subject options and thorough study of design history, business management and ceramic technology. Visual studies, including drawing and design is an essential part of the course.

SCOTLAND

Aberdeen

Grays School of Art
Robert Gordons Institute of Technology
Garthdee Road, Aberdeen AB9 2QD
Tel: Aberdeen 313247
(STD code 0224)

BA (Hons) and BA(CNAA) degrees in Design and Craft; Ceramics as main or subsidiary subject. Entry qualifications: 3 SCE 'H's incl. English + 2 'O's or 2 GCE 'A's incl. English + 3 'O's. This course provides students with the opportunity of carrying out, in ceramic processes, creative formal ideas which investigate two- and three-dimensional composition. Techniques experienced: thrown pottery; slab-ware; hand building; slip-casting and press-moulding; designing and making architectural relief tiles and mural panels; methods of surface decoration; colour and glazing and kiln firing. Facilities available for experimental out-door kiln building and firing including saltglazing and raku.

Dundee

Duncan of Jordanston College of Art
School of Design, Perth Road
Dundee DD1 4HT
Tel: Dundee 23261
(STD code 0382)

Degree course/pottery & ceramics 3 years. Foundation course + normally 2'A's + 3 'O's or 3 SCE 'H's + 2 SCE 'O's. BA/BA Hons. Degree

Edinburgh

Edinburgh College of Art
School of Design & Crafts
Lauriston Place
Edinburgh EH3 9DF
Tel: Edinburgh 229 9311
(STD code 031)

Degree course/ceramics BA(Hons) 3 SCE 'H's inc. Eng. 2 SCE 'O's (C band or above). 2 GCE 'A's 3 GCE 'O's (inc. Eng. at 'A' or 'O'). The department aims to provide an input of manipulative skills and technical information running parallel to the development of each student's creative personality. Initially, set projects familiarise the students with a rar of hand and machine processes applied to both form and surface design, greater emphasis being placed on self programmir the course develops. Clay, glaze and kiln theory and practice are thoroughly covere and a programme of relevant historical stu is undertaken through lectures, museum v and personal research. The department ai to foster a professional attitude in the students whether they regard themselves artists, craftsmen or designers.

Glasgow	**Glasgow School of Art** 167 Renfrew Street, Glasgow G3 6RQ Tel: Glasgow 332 9797 (STD code 041)	BA(Hons)/BA Design

NORTHERN IRELAND

Belfast	**University of Ulster** Department of Applied and Decorative Art York Street, Belfast Tel: Belfast 228515 (STD code 0232)	BA(Hons) Fine Craft Design. Study Areas: Ceramics, Silversmithing & Jewellery, Embroidery. This provides a unit based co across the whole Faculty including Design, Fine Art and Textiles/Fashion common to ₃ first year students. The ability to "specialis exists in years two and three. Equally, stud may wish to extend in second and third ye units taken in first year.

Post Graduate Courses in Ceramics

London	**Goldsmiths' College** New Cross, SE14 6NW Tel: 01-692 7171	Advanced Diploma in Art & Design ceram
	Royal College of Art Kensington Gore SW7 2EU Tel: 01-584-5020	Royal College of Art MA/M Des Ceramics and Glass 2 year course Craft Ceramics. Decoration. Research into mixed materials and technology.
Stoke-on-Trent	**North Staffordshire Polytechnic** Department of Design (Ceramics) College Road, Stoke on Trent Staffordshire ST4 2DE Tel: Stoke on Trent 45531 (STD code 0782)	MA Design 2 year sandwich course. Studer are expected to have developed a strong commitment to their work through previo experience and to follow very largely a personal programme of study. The course includes a period of industrial placement ar is supported by the award of DES Bursarie
Cardiff	**South Glamorgan Institute of** **Higher Education Faculty of** **Art & Design** Howard Gardens, Cardiff CF2 1SP Tel: Cardiff 55111 (STD code 0222)	MA Ceramics

Aberdeen	**Grays School of Art** Robert Gordons Institute of Technology Garthdee Road, Aberdeen AB9 2QD Tel: Aberdeen 313247 (STD code 0224)	Ceramics with Sculpture 1 yr post graduate diploma. Diploma of Art or BA CNAA
Edinburgh	**Edinburgh College of Art** School of Design & Crafts Lauriston Place, Edinburgh EH3 9DF Tel: Edinburgh 229 9311 (STD code 031)	Diploma in Ceramics. A one year course normally requiring good honours degree for entrance, for which applicants must submit detailed proposal.
Glasgow	**Glasgow School of Art** 167 Renfrew Street, Glasgow G3 6RQ Tel: Glasgow 332 9797 (STD code 041)	1 year degree course. MA (Design) 4 terms
Belfast	**University of Ulster** Department of Applied and Decorative Art York Street, Belfast Tel: Belfast 228515 (STD code 0232)	Postgraduate diploma in Art & Design. Students may select any area of study within the Faculty excluding Fine Art (which offers an MA Degree).

Part-time Tuition

Part-time courses

Part-time courses are generally classed as 'Non-vocational' though some are able, over a period of time, to provide a fairly thorough training in studio pottery techniques. Many Art Colleges, Technical Colleges and Colleges of Adult and Further Education (including some of the ones listed later) offer such courses, some giving their own certificate of proficiency. As the intake is irregular and the age and standard of students variable it is usual for each student to follow his/her own course of indefinite duration. Particulars of these and evening institutes in your area can be obtained from the local Adult Education Centre or from the Chief Education Officer of your Education Authority.

Evening and part-time classes

Most Local Education Authorities provide classes of this kind for beginners and also for the more advanced student. Classes last approximately 2 hours. Fees are relatively low. Materials are provided and finished work can be purchased at a minimal cost. Personal tools are not usually provided. Instructors vary in skill and teaching ability and it is worth asking other students how they have fared. Full information on available classes can be obtained from your local Public Library or Education Office. In London the booklet 'Floodlight' lists all currently available classes and can be obtained through most newsagents and bookshops. New sessions start in September each year. It is worth remembering that pottery classes are usually the most popular so book early. However, some vacant places will occur during the year which can be taken up by new students.

Short courses

Art Colleges do not generally offer 'crash' courses; however a number of short (usually summer) courses are offered by public and private bodies and by individual potters. Particulars of these should be sought in the national educational or art press or in periodicals such as 'Ceramic Review', 'Pottery Quarterly' and 'Crafts'. Some potters run summer courses which may or may not be residential. Such courses are not cheap, but give excellent value for money. Equipment is good and the prospectus lists the aims of the course and the timetable. It may be worthwhile shopping around for the course that suits you best. Some of the well known potters' merchants run seminars for the amateur and professional potter. The National Institute of Adult Education publishes a booklet "Residential Short Courses" twice a year in January and August. It can be obtained for £1 from National Institute of Continuing Adult Education 19b De Montford Street, Leicester, LE1 7GE.

Craftsmen Potters Association Activities

Exhibitions 1983-1985
Craftsmen Potters Shop, 7 Marshall Street, London WI

1983
New Members: Ian Byers, Miguel Espinosa, John Huggins, David Miller,
Angela Verdon, Takeshi Yasuda (March)
New Stoneware Pots: Janet Leach (April)
Decorated Porcelain: Bill Brown, Sheila Casson, Emmanuel Cooper, Sally Dawson,
Dorothy Feibleman, Jane Hamlyn, David Lloyd Jones, Eileen Lewenstein,
David Leach, Eileen Nisbet, Colin Pearson, Christine-Ann Richards, Mary Rogers,
Geoffrey Swindell, Poh Chap Yeap (June)
Studio Ceramics Today (Victoria and Albert Museum) (September)
Four from Farnham: Henry Hammond, Siddig El'Nigoumi, Paul Barron,
Nigel Wood (September)
Ewen Henderson, Janice Tchalenko (October)

1984
New Members: Clive Bowen, Daphne Carnegy, Richard Launder,
Magdalene Odundo, David Scott, Sabina.Teuteberg, Caroline Whyman (February)
The Individual Eye: Graham Burr, Ruth King, Magdalene Odundo,
Geoffrey Swindell, Joanna Constantinidis (April)
Especially for the Table: Members Exhibition (June)
People and Other Animals: Maggie Berkowitz, Audrey Blackman, Barbara Colls,
Tessa Fuchs, Alan Heaps, Neil Ions, Eric James Mellon, Stanislas Reychan, Rosemary
Wren, Peter Crotty, Andrew McGarva, Dave Edmonds (October)
Alan Caiger-Smith and Aldermaston Pottery (November)

1985
New Members: John Ablitt, John Dunn, John Gibson, Anthony Phillips, Henry Pim,
John Wheeldon (February)
Playing with Fire: Margery Clinton, Peter Dick, Micky Doherty, David Miller,
Dave Roberts (April)
New Work: David Scott, Sabina Teuteberg (May)
Stoneware and Porcelain: David Lloyd Jones, Takeshi Yasuda (June)
Shades of Blue (July)
Hungarian Ceramics Today (September)
John Glick: Pots from the New World (October)
Stanislas Reychan: Retrospective (October)
John Ward: New Work (November)

Craftsmen Potters Association Events

1984

Visits to Ray Finch at Winchcombe Pottery and to Russell Collins pottery at Hook Norton (June)

Residential Weekend at Keele University, Stoke on Trent: Aspects of Marketing (September)

Visits to Fitzwilliam Museum and Kettles Yard House and Gallery, Cambridge (December)

1985

John Glick: Two Day Workshop (September)

Craftsmen Potters Association Evening Meetings 1983-1985

1983

Oliver Watson: Victoria and Albert Museum Collection of Contemporary Ceramics (February)
Joan Weissman: Porcelain and Potters in New Mexico (April)
Nigel Wood: Shanghai Conference on Ancient Chinese Pottery and Porcelain (May)
Henry Pim: Methods and Techniques (August)
Peter Lane: Potting, Pots and Potters (September)

1984

Maria Kresz: Slide lecture and film — Hungarian Pottery, Past and Present (January)
Matthias Osterman: Canadian Potter (March)
Anne Holian: Enamel Decoration (April)
Rosemary Wren and Peter Crotty: Denise and Henry Wren at Oxshott Pottery (May)
Harry Davis: Whence and Whither (May)
Alan Peascod: Lustre and Dry Glaze Technology and the Islamic Theme (August)
Alan Caiger-Smith: Lustre and Light (November)

1985

Thomas Edward Sellen: In Search of Shibui (January)
Sandy Brown: Life in a Lively Pottery in Mashiko (April)
James Tower: Sculptural Pots (May)
Matthias Osterman: Canadian Ceramics (June)
Mary White: European Ceramics — Germany (June)
Imre Schrammel: Hungarian Ceramics (September)
Ljerka Njers: Yugoslavian Ceramics (October)

Craftsmen Potters Association of Great Britain Ltd.

President — Pamela, Lady Glenconner
Secretary — David Winkley
Treasurer — John Awdry

Council 1986
Chairman — David Roberts
Vice-Chairman — David Frith
Emmanuel Cooper
Dorothy Feibleman
John Gibson
Ruth King
Eileen Lewenstein
Jim Robison
Peter Smith
Sabina Teuteberg
David Winkley
Andrew Young

Association
Accounts — Harry Davey
Secretary — Vanessa Wills

Craftsmen Potters Shop
Manager — Vivien Whitaker
Assistants — Rebecca Beesley
Anne Holian
Laurie Porter

Ceramic Review
Editors — Eileen Lewenstein
Emmanuel Cooper

Editorial Assistant, Advertising — Daphne Matthews
Subscriptions and Books — Marilyn Brown
Assistant — John Brooksbank

Useful Addresses

Craftsmen Potters Association
William Blake House
7 Marshall Street
London WIV IFD

Crafts Council
12 Waterloo Place
London SWI 4AU

**Council of Small Industries in
Rural Areas (CoSIRA)**
141 Castle Street
Salisbury
Wilts SP1 3TB

Welsh Arts Council
53 Charles Street
Cardiff CFI 4ED

Scottish Arts Council
19 Charlotte Square
Edinburgh

Design Council
Pearl Assurance House
Greyfriars Road
Cardiff CFI 3JN

Design Council
Windsor House
9-15 Bedford Street
Belfast BT2 7EG

Design Council
28 Haymarket
London SWIY 4SU

British Crafts Centre
43 Earlham Street
London WC2H 9LD

Highland Craftpoint
Beauly
Inverness-shire IV4 7EH

Ceramic Review
21 Carnaby Street
London WIV IPH

Midland Arts Centre
Cannon Hill Park
Birmingham BI2 9QH

The Royal Exchange Craft Centre
Manchester M2 7DH

Scottish Design Council
72 St. Vincent Place
Glasgow G2 5TN

Scottish Craft Centre
140 Cannongate
Edinburgh

Regional Arts Associations

Eastern Arts Association
8/9 Bridge Street
Cambridge

South East Arts Association
58 London Road
Southborough
Tunbridge Wells
Kent

East Midland Arts Association
1 Frederick Street
Loughborough
Leicestershire

Greater London Arts Association
25 Tavistock Place
London WCIH 9SE

**Lincolnshire and Humberside
Arts Association**
Beaumont Lodge
Beaumont Fee
Lincoln

Merseyside Arts Association
Bluecoat Chambers
School Lane
Liverpool

Northern Arts Association
31 Newbridge Street
Newcastle-upon-Tyne

North West Arts Association
52 King Street
Manchester M2 4LY

Useful Addresses

Regional Arts Associations continued . . .

Southern Arts Association
19 Southgate
Winchester

South West Arts Association
23 Southern Hay East
Exeter

West Midlands Arts Association
City Arcade
Birmingham B2 4TX

Yorkshire Arts Association
Glyde House
Glydegate
Bradford 5

North Wales Arts Association
Victoria Street
Cwmbran
Gwent NP4 3JP

West Wales Arts Association
Dark Gate, Red Street
Carmarthen
Dyfed

INTRODUCING MICROWAVE COMBINATION COOKERY

Jan Harris

ANGELL EDITIONS

Newton Abbot, Devon